The Cathode Ray Revolution

PHILIP KOGAN M.Sc. JOAN PICK B.Sc.

FOUNDATIONS OF SCIENCE LIBRARY

GREYSTONE PRESS/NEW YORK · TORONTO · LONDON

This new presentation assembles freshly edited material from
'Understanding Science' on one subject into a single volume.

Copyright © MCMLXVI Sampson Low, Marston & Co. Ltd.

Library of Congress Catalog Card Number: 66–14641

Printed in Great Britain
Manufactured in U.S.A.

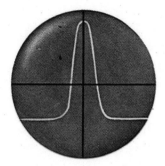

CONTENTS

PART ONE

Introducing Valves

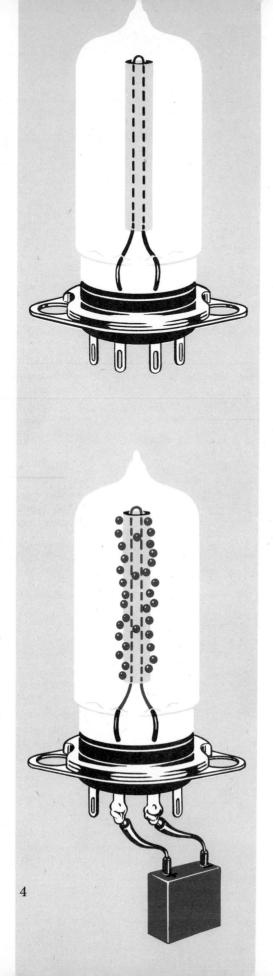

Thermionic Emission and the Diode Valve

A CURRENT of electricity flowing in a wire consists of *electrons* jumping from one atom to the next all the way along the wire. These electrons (tiny negatively-charged particles) come from the outermost parts of the metal atoms which make up the wire. They are known as 'free' electrons to distinguish them from the other, more tightly held, electrons which also form part of the atoms. If two bare wires laid side by side (but not touching) are connected to a battery, no current flows between them (unless the battery is large enough to cause sparks). The free electrons cannot break out of the wires. The working of a radio valve, however, depends upon such electrons being completely free and able to move through the empty space which separates the various parts of the valve.

Although free electrons can drift along a metal wire they cannot easily escape from its surface. This is because of the forces of attraction exerted on each free electron by the surrounding atoms. An electron inside the wire is surrounded on all sides by atoms. The surrounding atoms try to 'pull' the electron in every direction, with the result that they cancel each other out. An electron at the surface of the wire, however, has no metal atoms on one side of it. (The atoms — or strictly speaking groups of atoms called molecules — in air are so widely scattered that their effects are negligible.) This means that *all* the forces of attraction are trying to pull the electron back into the wire.

Upper picture shows the cathode of a thermionic valve. The cathode is a metal sleeve whose outer surface is coated with barium oxide and strontium oxide. *Lower picture:* When the cathode is heated (by passing a current through a fine wire filament inside the sleeve) *electrons* are emitted from the oxides, forming a cloud around the cathode.

4

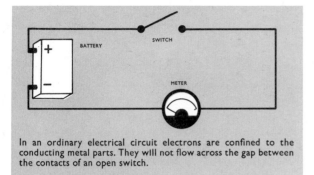

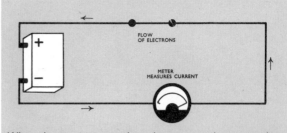

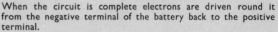

In an ordinary electrical circuit electrons are confined to the conducting metal parts. They will not flow across the gap between the contacts of an open switch.

When the circuit is complete electrons are driven round it from the negative terminal of the battery back to the positive terminal.

Only a few very 'energetic' electrons manage to break through the barrier of attractive forces and escape from the surface. Free electrons can be made more 'energetic' in a number of ways so that they have a better chance of breaking away. The usual method of energizing them is merely to heat the wire in which they are contained by passing an electric current through it. In the filament of an ordinary electric lamp the free electrons move about so vigorously that some of them escape from the hot filament altogether. They are, so to speak, 'boiled out' of the filament. In a lamp the escaping electrons congregate uselessly in an invisible cloud around the filament. In a radio valve they are pulled across to a metal plate (the anode), because this is arranged to be more 'electrically positive' than the filament and the positive charges on the plate attract the opposite (negative) charges of the electrons.

The number of electrons breaking out of a hot wire depends upon two factors — the temperature of the wire (the number increases enormously as the temperature is raised) and the material the wire is made from. Some materials allow free electrons to escape easily; others exert such a strong force of attraction on their free electrons that the electrons need to take in a great deal of energy before they can break through the surface 'barrier'. A mixture of thorium and carbon alloyed with tungsten is one material that has a fairly small surface barrier effect; a mixture of barium oxide and strontium oxide is another. Both of these are used as *cathodes* (sources of electrons) in valves.

(A mixture of barium oxide and strontium oxide will not carry a current — it has to be heated *indirectly* by painting it onto a sleeve which surrounds a white-hot filament.)

The number of electrons released from the cathode depends on the material and its temperature.

THE ANODE OF A THERMIONIC VALVE

The electrons form a negatively charged cloud, called a *space charge*, around the wire. The majority of modern radio valves use *indirectly heated cathodes* in which the filament wire is used merely to heat a sleeve coated with materials that emit electrons easily. To be of any use the electrons have to be drawn across the empty space between the heated filament (or cathode) and another part of the valve called the anode (or plate).

Electrons are drawn across the empty space by making the anode electrically positive — i.e. it is short of electrons, and in trying to make good this shortage it exerts an attraction on the cloud of electrons (the space charge) around the cathode. The anode can be made electrically positive by connecting it to the positive terminal of a high-voltage battery. The negative terminal of the battery is connected to the cathode.

The movement of electrons from the cathode to the anode carries a current of electricity across the valve. Since the anode is cold it does not emit electrons. The current therefore flows across the valve in one direction only.

5

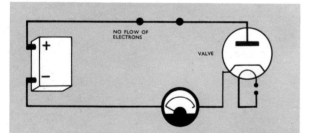

A valve is like an open switch: its two electrical connections are completely separate and there is an empty space between them.

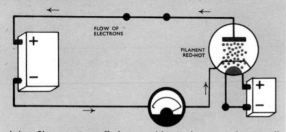

A hot filament gives off electrons (this is thermionic 'emission') which are not confined to conducting metal parts—they are free to move through empty space. Here the battery drives them across the valve which therefore acts like a closed switch.

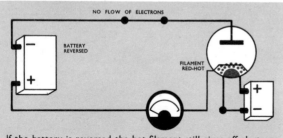

If the battery is reversed the hot filament still gives off electrons but they do not reach the other side of the valve. In this case the valve acts like an open switch and no current flows in the circuit

A diode valve in an electrical circuit acts in much the same way as a stop-cock in a water pipe. It controls the size of the current flowing through it, and it can stop the current altogether. If this was all the valve could do it would find few, if any, practical applications, for currents can be controlled more cheaply by switches and variable resistors (called rheostats) like the volume control on a radio receiver. But the diode can do more than a stop-cock or a switch. Its value lies in the fact that it only allows currents to flow through it in one direction. In other words it is a *valve*.

A simple switch has two electrical connections, one through which the current enters and one through which the current leaves. Similarly a diode has two electrical connections (or *electrodes*): one is the *cathode*, the other is the *anode*.

HOW THE DIODE CONDUCTS

A modern diode valve may have eight or nine connecting pins sticking out of its base. This ensures that it fits securely into a standard valve-holder. But only four of the pins are actually electrical connections. One leads to the anode, one leads to the cathode and the other two lead to the filament or heater.

The filament or heater is a fine tungsten wire like the filament of an electric light bulb—though it is not coiled. A fairly strong current (either A.C. or D.C.) is passed through the filament to make it red-hot or almost white-hot. The filament is stretched between the base of the valve and a support near the top. The cathode is a metal sleeve surrounding the filament but not quite touching it. Heat radiated out from the filament raises the temperature of the cathode, so that the mixture of barium oxide and strontium oxide coating the outside surface of the cathode throws out electrons (this is the *thermionic effect*).

The cloud of electrons is turned into a flow of electrons by making the anode attract them. The anode is a flattened hollow cylinder made of nickel which surrounds the cathode. The space between the anode and the cathode is empty (since all the air has been removed from the valve), and the electrons emitted by the hot cathode have to be pulled across this empty space. Electrons are pulled to the anode only when it is *positively* charged, for the positive charges on the anode exert a force of attraction on the negatively charged electrons. Positive charges are put on to the anode by applying a voltage between the anode and cathode. A large dry battery, with its positive terminal connected to the anode and its negative terminal connected to the cathode, very conveniently provides the necessary voltage. *(See pages 8-9.)*

The battery and its connections form a circuit which is broken only by the valve itself. Electrons are pulled across from the cathode to the anode, thereby bridging the break in the circuit. A sensitive ammeter placed anywhere in the circuit shows that a small current is flowing. If the battery is reversed, however, no current is recorded by the ammeter. The electron cloud is still being formed but now the anode is negatively

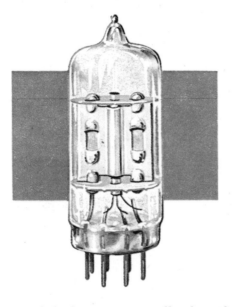

An actual diode is a very small valve. The filament stretches up the centre of the valve. It is surrounded by the cathode sleeve which is itself surrounded by the anode.

charged and repels electrons instead of pulling them across the valve. If the current supply to the heater is cut off, even though the anode is made positive and the cathode made negative, the ammeter again shows that no current is flowing in the anode circuit. This is because the cathode will not emit electrons when it is cold. There is no electron cloud for the anode to pull across the valve, so once again the valve acts as a break in the circuit.

Although using a battery to make the anode positive is convenient and fairly reliable, it is generally cheaper to use the mains supply instead. But the mains supply in most countries is in the form of an *alternating current* (A.C.) which changes its direction about a hundred times every second. If the valve were connected to an A.C. supply instead of to a battery, its anode would be made positive for one-hundredth of a second, then negative for the next one-hundredth of a second. Electrons would be pulled across the valve in a series of jerks, for there would be no flow while the anode was negative. In order to pull the electrons across the valve in a continuous stream the alternating voltage of the A.C. mains supply has to be turned into a steady one-way voltage like that provided by a battery. This process is called *rectification*. *(See page 44.)*

VARYING THE VOLTAGES

The current which flows through a copper wire (or any other conductor of electricity) is proportional to the voltage between the ends of the wire. The voltage is the difference in electrical pressure which drives electrons along the wire. The current is the rate at which electrons flow. The greater the voltage, the greater is the current—this is what *Ohm's law* states. But Ohm's law *does not apply to radio valves*, for radio valves are not conductors in the ordinary sense.

If we connect a battery to a radio valve so that the negative terminal is joined to the cathode and the positive terminal is joined to the anode, a meter placed anywhere in the circuit will show that provided the cathode is heated a current is flowing. When the battery is removed no current flows (diagram *i*, page 10). The heated cathode gives off electrons but they stay in a cloud (the space charge) around the cathode. Very few, if any, of the electrons reach the anode. The cloud of electrons swarming around the cathode repels newly released electrons (like charges repel each other) back to the cathode. So to all intents and purposes the valve is a break in the circuit.

When the battery is replaced, the cathode is made negative and the anode is made positive. In other words there is a voltage across the valve. If this voltage is small (diagram *ii*) the meter shows that a small current is flowing. The positive anode is attracting electrons from the outermost parts of the space charge. Electrons actually move through the empty space between the cathode and the anode.

When the voltage across the valve is increased by adding another battery (diagram *iii*) the meter shows that the current flowing has been very much increased. The anode is now sufficiently positive to pull a great many electrons out of the space charge. The size of the space charge is therefore reduced and it is therefore less effective in repelling electrons back into the cathode. When the anode voltage is low the space charge limits the number of electrons reaching the anode.

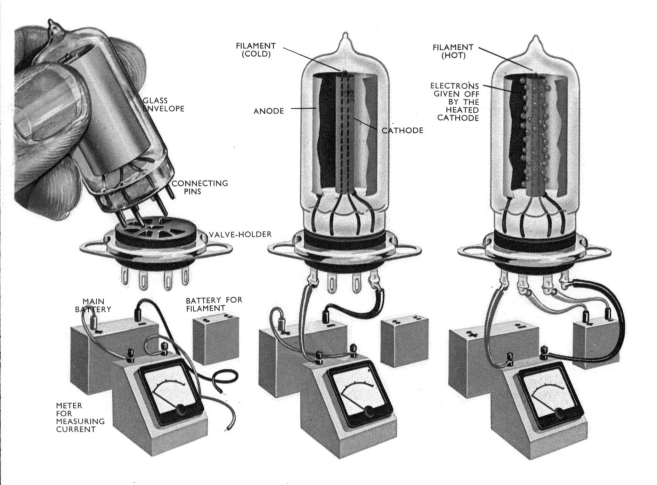

Components used in demonstrating the diode valve. The *meter* measures current in thousandths of an amp (milliamps).

The anode and cathode are correctly wired to a battery. No current flows because the cathode is cold.

The cathode is heated and emits electrons. No current flows because there is nothing to pull the electrons to the anode.

When the voltage is increased again by adding a third battery (diagram *iv*) the meter shows another big increase in current. Actually at this stage the increase in current is proportional to the increase in voltage so the valve is acting as a copper wire would act. Now the anode is attracting electrons from the cathode through the space charge and the repelling effect of the space charge is very small.

Adding a fourth battery (diagram *v*) to increase the voltage produces another big increase in the current—but not quite as big as before. Now the repelling effect of the space charge has been completely overcome. Adding a fifth battery (diagram *vi*) produces an unexpectedly small increase in current. This is because the reservoir of electrons in the space charge has been used up and now the electrons are pulled to the anode almost as fast as they are emitted by the cathode.

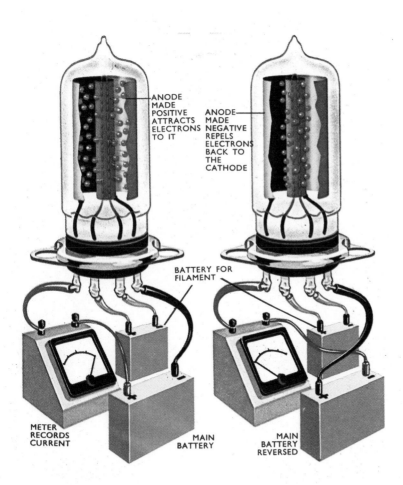

ANODE MADE POSITIVE ATTRACTS ELECTRONS TO IT

ANODE MADE NEGATIVE REPELS ELECTRONS BACK TO THE CATHODE

BATTERY FOR FILAMENT

METER RECORDS CURRENT

MAIN BATTERY

MAIN BATTERY REVERSED

The battery makes the anode positive so that it attracts electrons from the heated cathode. Meter now shows that current is flowing.

The battery has been reversed, making the anode negative so that it *repels* electrons. No current passes through the valve or the meter.

Adding a sixth (and final) battery produces only a minute increase in the current (diagram *vii*). Again the electrons are attracted to the anode as fast as they are emitted. Since the rate at which the cathode emits electrons has nothing to do with the anode voltage the current is practically the same as before. This condition is called *saturation*. Most valves are operated well below this region.

The rate at which the cathode emits electrons is governed by its temperature and the material from which it is made. By raising the temperature of the cathode it can be made to emit more electrons and so a greater current can be carried through the valve. The temperature of the cathode is raised by increasing the current flowing through its heater (filament). Diagrams *viii* to *xiv* show the experiment repeated

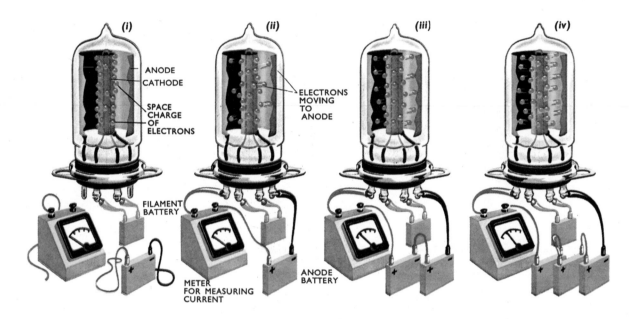

An experiment to show how the current flowing through a diode valve varies with the voltage of the anode. The voltage is increased in equal stages by adding on extra batteries one by one.

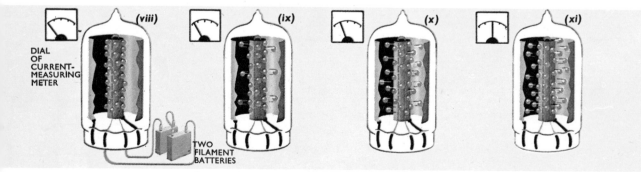

step by step as before. This time, however, the cathode is made much hotter than before. It emits electrons at a greater rate (i.e. more electrons per second) and consequently produces a much larger space charge than before. The current flowing with just one battery in the anode circuit is the same as it was in the first experiment. When the anode voltage is low the number of electrons reaching it is limited by the repelling effect of the space charge, and so the extra electrons given off from the hotter cathode do not contribute to any increase in the flow across the valve.

The size of the current produced by a high anode voltage (a large number of batteries) is obviously greater in the second experiment. This is because the space charge is much larger and forms a much bigger reservoir of electrons.

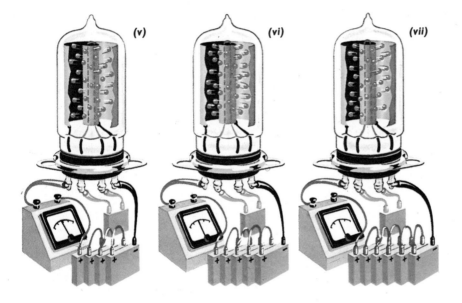

The diagrams (viii to xiv) below show the experiment repeated using two filament batteries to raise the temperature of the cathode.

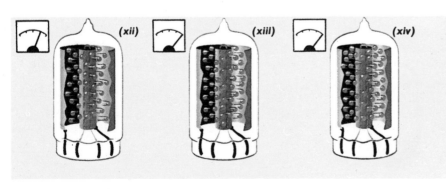

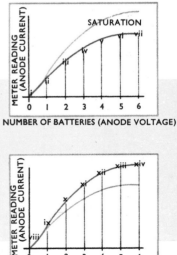

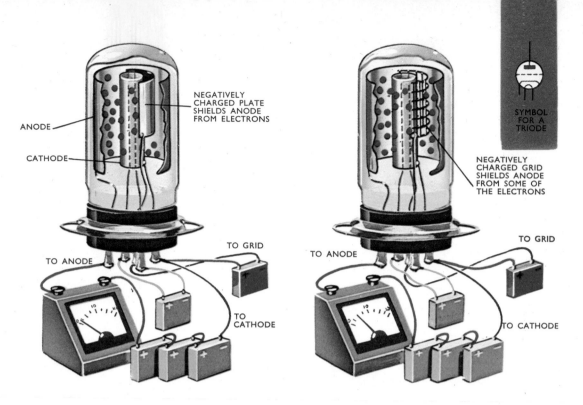

ANODE

CATHODE

NEGATIVELY
CHARGED PLATE
SHIELDS ANODE
FROM ELECTRONS

TO ANODE

TO GRID

TO CATHODE

NEGATIVELY
CHARGED GRID
SHIELDS ANODE
FROM SOME OF
THE ELECTRONS

TO ANODE

TO GRID

TO CATHODE

SYMBOL
FOR A
TRIODE

(Left) A third electrode inserted between the cathode and the anode repels electrons when it is negatively charged. *(Right)* If the third electrode is an open wire 'grid' some electrons can pass through it on their way to the anode.

The Triode Valve

THE DIODE valve has two electrodes —the cathode which emits electrons, and the anode (or 'plate') which collects electrons. Electrons flow in a steady stream across the empty space between the cathode and the anode, provided that the anode is positively charged. An inventor named Lee De Forest working in the United States hit upon the brilliant idea of inserting an open spiral of wire between the cathode and the anode. He

reasoned that electrons should pass easily through the spiral (or grid as it is called) when it is uncharged, but electrons should be repelled by the grid when it is negatively charged. Since electrons must pass through the grid in order to reach the anode, the number of electrons collected by the anode should be drastically reduced when the grid is given a negative charge. The valve which he invented is called the *triode* because it has *three* electrodes.

If the grid is given a positive charge it can draw electrons from the electron cloud (space charge) around the cathode. These electrons 'overshoot' the grid, passing right through it (since the turns in the spiral are widely spaced), and thus add to the number of electrons collected by the anode. In other words the pull of the anode is augmented by the pull of the grid. The grid is able to draw elec-

The Parts of a Triode Valve

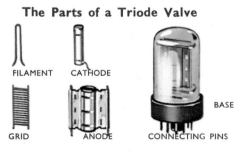

FILAMENT   CATHODE

GRID   ANODE   CONNECTING PINS

BASE

12

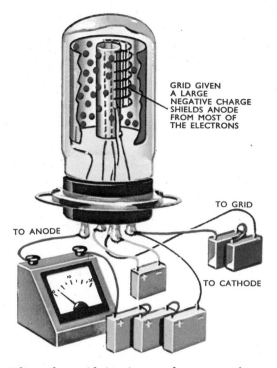

GRID GIVEN A LARGE NEGATIVE CHARGE SHIELDS ANODE FROM MOST OF THE ELECTRONS

TO GRID

TO ANODE

TO CATHODE

When the grid is given a large negative charge it repels most of the electrons back to the cathode.

trons from the space charge, even though it has only a small positive charge, simply because it is near to the cathode.

The flow of electrons from the cathode to the anode is called the *anode current*. Since the strength of the anode current is greatly affected by the 'positiveness' or 'negativeness' of the grid, this electrode is often called the *control* grid. Its importance lies in the fact that a *small* variation in the charge on the grid results

in a *large* variation in the anode current. The charges on the grid are put there by a difference of electrical voltage between the grid and the cathode. A circuit containing a battery can be connected (outside the valve, of course) to the grid to provide this voltage. If the *voltage* between the grid and the cathode varies, the anode *current* will vary in time with it, but to a much greater extent. This is the basis of *amplification*, the chief function of valves. (The diode valve cannot amplify because it has no grid.)

THE TRIODE VALVE AS AN AMPLIFIER

Because the grid of a triode valve is close to the cathode (the source of electrons) it has a very great effect upon the current passing through the valve (called the anode current). If the grid is given a big negative charge it repels electrons back to the cathode and no current flows through the valve. The important thing to remember about the grid is that a small change in its 'positiveness' or 'negativeness' can produce a big change in the anode current. The 'positiveness' or 'negativeness' of the grid is usually referred to as its voltage. Quite a small voltage making the grid negative can cut the anode current by half. The same reduction in anode current could be brought about by drastically reducing the voltage of the anode (which must have a certain 'positiveness'

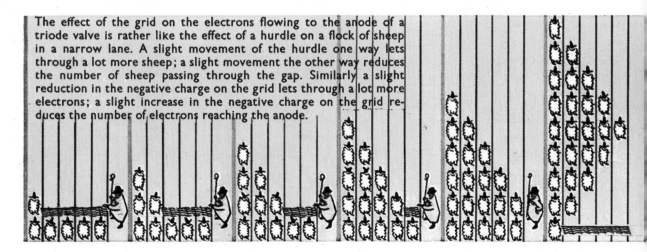

The effect of the grid on the electrons flowing to the anode of a triode valve is rather like the effect of a hurdle on a flock of sheep in a narrow lane. A slight movement of the hurdle one way lets through a lot more sheep; a slight movement the other way reduces the number of sheep passing through the gap. Similarly a slight reduction in the negative charge on the grid lets through a lot more electrons; a slight increase in the negative charge on the grid reduces the number of electrons reaching the anode.

or no current will flow through the valve).

Any given change in the anode current needs either a large change in the anode voltage or a small change in the grid voltage: the ratio of these two changes in voltage (change in anode voltage/change in grid voltage) is called the *amplification factor*.

Suppose that the triode is to be used for amplifying the tiny voltage delivered by a microphone. When sound waves fall on a microphone they cause a diaphragm to vibrate. The voltage delivered by the microphone fluctuates in time with the vibrations of the diaphragm, and in most cases it is an *alternating voltage*. In other words, each outlet terminal of the microphone is alternately positive and then negative. The alternating voltage could be fed onto the grid of the triode to make it alternately positive and then negative. The alternating voltage of the grid would produce big *fluctuations* in the anode current (since the current

flowing through a valve cannot change its direction it cannot be called an *alternating* current even though it may fluctuate in a regular manner).

Unfortunately this scheme in which the grid is alternately positive and negative does not work well in practice. The grid must not be allowed to become positive. For one thing a positive grid acts like an anode and collects electrons so that a current flows in the grid circuit. This 'grid current' represents a waste of electrical energy. Secondly, the fluctuations in the anode current would be very distorted, i.e. they would not be a faithful replica of the alternating voltage supplied by the microphone. To see why this is so, take a look at the graph which shows how the anode current varies with the grid voltage. When the grid is positive and when it is uncharged the graph is curved. But a section of the graph where the grid is negative is practically a straight line. This means that changes in the

Diagrams below and on next page show how voltage variations from microphone affect the current flowing through a triode valve.

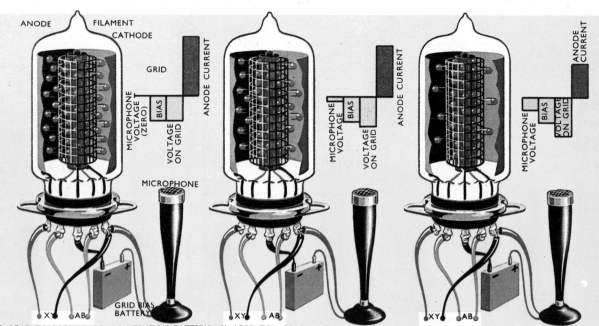

X LEAD TO POSITIVE OF HIGH TENSION BATTERY   Y=LEAD TO NEGATIVE OF HIGH TENSION BATTERY   A AND B=LEADS TO FILAMENT BAT

14

anode current are directly proportional to changes in the (negative) grid voltage. So in order to achieve amplification without distortion it is necessary to keep to the linear (straight) portion of the graph. This is done by connecting a *grid bias battery* to give the grid a steady negative charge. The alternating voltage from the microphone is superimposed on the steady voltage of the bias battery so that although the combined voltage varies (in time with the vibrations of the

diaphragm in the microphone) it never reverses. For example the voltage from the microphone during one-thousandth of a second might be 0, +1, +3, +1, 0, −1, −3, −1, 0 volts. If this alternating voltage was superimposed on a steady voltage of −6 volts from a grid bias battery the combined voltage during the same period would be −6, −5, −3, −5, −6, −7, −9, −7, −6 volts. So although the combined voltage is always negative it shows exactly the same variations as the alternating voltage from the micro-phone. If this combined voltage were fed to the grid in a triode it would control the flow of electrons passing between cathode and anode in such a way that the resulting anode current fluctuated in exactly the same manner. The actual values of the anode current may be quite small (a few thousandths of an amp). When it flows through a high resistance (called the load) in the anode circuit it produces a considerable voltage (much greater than the grid voltage) between the ends of the load. From Ohm's law the voltage between the ends of the load is equal to the current multiplied by the

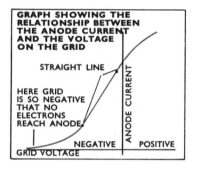

GRAPH SHOWING THE RELATIONSHIP BETWEEN THE ANODE CURRENT AND THE VOLTAGE ON THE GRID

STRAIGHT LINE

HERE GRID IS SO NEGATIVE THAT NO ELECTRONS REACH ANODE

ANODE CURRENT

NEGATIVE   POSITIVE

GRID VOLTAGE

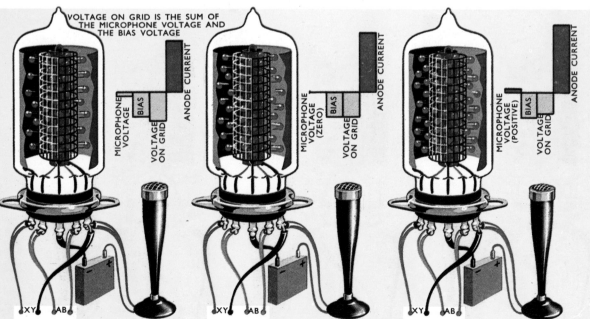

VOLTAGE ON GRID IS THE SUM OF THE MICROPHONE VOLTAGE AND THE BIAS VOLTAGE

MICROPHONE VOLTAGE   BIAS   VOLTAGE ON GRID   ANODE CURRENT

MICROPHONE VOLTAGE (ZERO)   BIAS   VOLTAGE ON GRID   ANODE CURRENT

MICROPHONE VOLTAGE (POSITIVE)   BIAS   VOLTAGE ON GRID   ANODE CURRENT

D TO POSITIVE OF HIGH TENSION BATTERY   Y=LEAD TO NEGATIVE OF HIGH TENSION BATTERY   A AND B= LEADS TO FILAMENT BATTERY

15

resistance of the load. If the resistance is high the voltage will be high even though the current is small. The battery in the anode circuit alone supplies the energy needed to pull electrons across the valve and hence the increase or *amplification* of voltage is obtained at the expense of this battery. The grid circuit does not contribute any energy.

AN AUDIO FREQUENCY AMPLIFIER

Vibrations in the air can be heard by most people as a sound if the number of vibrations per second (the frequency) is not less than 20 and not greater than 15,000. A microphone produces electrical 'vibrations' (usually variations in voltage) which have exactly the same frequency as the sound vibrations falling on

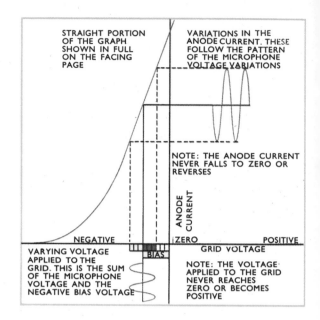

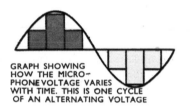

GRAPH SHOWING HOW THE MICROPHONE VOLTAGE VARIES WITH TIME. THIS IS ONE CYCLE OF AN ALTERNATING VOLTAGE

the microphone. An audio frequency amplifier is designed to magnify variations in voltage which lie within the range 20 to 15,000 cycles (complete vibrations) per second.

The basic audio frequency amplifier consists of a triode valve, three batteries

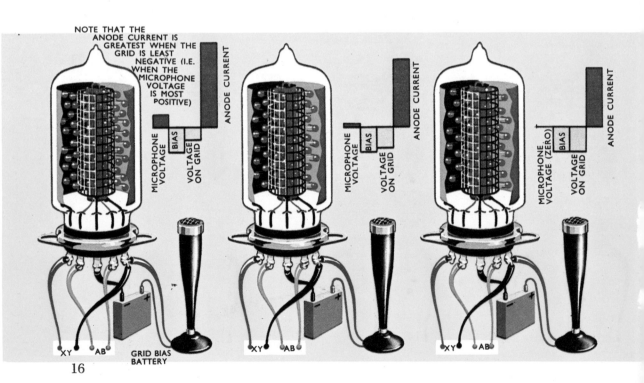

NOTE THAT THE ANODE CURRENT IS GREATEST WHEN THE GRID IS LEAST NEGATIVE (I.E. WHEN THE MICROPHONE VOLTAGE IS MOST POSITIVE)

GRID BIAS BATTERY

and a resistor. The *low tension* (low voltage) battery is used to heat the *filament* of the valve. The *grid bias* battery is used to keep the *grid* negatively charged, since distortion and waste of power might result if the grid became positively charged. The *high tension* (high voltage) battery is used to keep the *anode* positively charged so that it attracts electrons from the cathode. The *resistor* is usually a short length of compressed carbon, which, as its name suggests, offers resistance to any current passing through it. It is connected between the anode and the positive terminal of the high tension battery, forming what is known as the *load*.

The input signal (e.g. the variations in voltage delivered by a microphone) is connected to the grid by way of the grid bias battery. The signal is superimposed on the steady voltage of the grid bias battery so that the voltage of the grid itself varies in time with the signal, yet is always negative when compared with the cathode. Variations in the voltage of the grid *control* the current flowing through the valve. For when the grid is very negative it repels all electrons back to the cathode and no current flows. (This is not allowed to happen in this simple kind of amplifier.) The current flowing through the valve, through the load resistor, and through the high tension battery back to the cathode, varies in strength exactly in time with the variations in the voltage of the grid. A current flowing through the load resistor produces a drop in voltage across it. In other words the end where the current leaves the resistor is more positive than the end where it enters. The size of the voltage drop can easily be calculated by multiplying the current (in amps) by the resistance (in ohms) of the load. *Variations* in the anode current produce variations in the voltage drop across the load and these voltage variations are a replica of the input signal. If the load has a high resistance the voltage variations across it will be big, certainly much bigger than the voltage variations of the input signal.

The output of the amplifier is simply the voltage across the load. This is generally fed to the grid of a second valve for further amplification. To feed it directly to a loudspeaker would not be very satisfactory since, although the voltage has been amplified, the *power* (i.e. current times voltage) is still very small.

In the practical audio frequency amplifier illustrated overleaf, two *capacitors* have been added. Each capacitor is basically a pair of metal plates separated by an insulating layer, so it will not allow currents to pass through it. It will, however, allow voltage *variations* to pass. The action of a capacitor is rather like that of a rubber sheet stretched across a water pipe. The sheet prevents any actual flow of water, but because it is elastic changes in *pressure* on one side of the sheet are transmitted to the water on the other side. (Voltage in electricity corresponds to pressure in liquids.)

If, as is often the case, the input comes from the *anode* of another valve (which must of course be connected to the positive terminal of its own high tension battery), the grid would be made positive. The capacitor in the grid circuit *isolates* the grid from such a steady voltage and thus prevents it from becoming positive. The capacitor in the output circuit isolates the grid of the next valve from the steady positive voltage of the high tension battery.

VALVE CHARACTERISTICS

Electronic valves deal with currents and voltages. By controlling a current flow, the *triode valve* is able to *amplify* voltages. Before a new type of valve is put on the market, it must be tested to see what it does to currents and voltages fed

Basic audio frequency amplifier circuit.

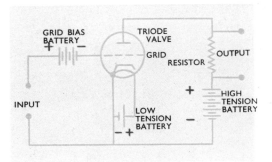

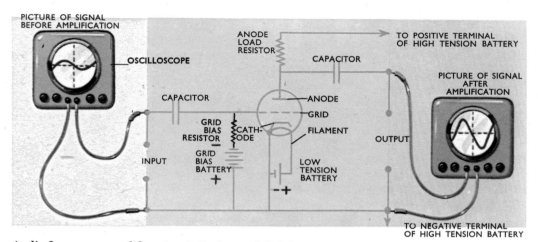

PICTURE OF SIGNAL
BEFORE AMPLIFICATION

OSCILLOSCOPE

ANODE
LOAD
RESISTOR

TO POSITIVE TERMINAL
OF HIGH TENSION BATTERY

CAPACITOR

PICTURE OF SIGNAL
AFTER
AMPLIFICATION

CAPACITOR

ANODE

GRID

GRID
BIAS
RESISTOR

CATH-
ODE

FILAMENT

OUTPUT

INPUT

GRID
BIAS
BATTERY

LOW
TENSION
BATTERY

TO NEGATIVE TERMINAL
OF HIGH TENSION BATTERY

Audio frequency amplifier circuit. In the model of the circuit shown on the right, the components have been arranged to correspond with the circuit diagram. In practice the layout would be very different.

into the valve. The valve is designed to work within a certain range of currents and voltages. It is connected into a test circuit, where the currents and voltages in and out of the valve can be controlled, regulated, and measured. In simple laboratory test equipment, the circuit is similar to an actual amplifying circuit. The differences are that the resistors setting the voltages of grid and anode are *variable,* and that the circuit contains three measuring instruments — two voltmeters for measuring the grid and anode voltages and an ammeter for measuring the current collected by the anode.

Manufacturers have large, push-button valve testers, where there are many more dials, and where the results can be displayed automatically on an oscilloscope screen.

In practice, the signal to be amplified by the valve is an alternating signal usually fed into it through the grid. The signal is the varying voltage between the grid and the cathode. A direct current is

used instead of an alternating current when the characteristics are being found. The value of the direct current is kept steady while readings are made: then it is altered to a new value, simulating the effect of a varying, alternating current.

The results of the tests are plotted on graph paper as two sets of curves, called characteristic curves, or simply *characteristics.* These give the electronic engineer practically all the information he needs to know about the performance of the valve — how it amplifies, and the values of currents and voltages at which it works best.

Three measuring instruments are used, giving three sets of readings of currents and voltages. On a single graph it is impossible to show how more than two quantities vary at the same time. So while the values are being tested, the circuit is adjusted so that one of the measuring instruments, either the ammeter or one of the voltmeters, gives the same reading all the time. Then the other two can be varied. The readings for one of them are plotted on the horizontal 'x' axis of the graph, and the other up the vertical 'y' axis of the graph. The reading of the third instrument is kept steady until a set of readings for the first two has been made, over the working range of the valve.

One of the characteristics shows the variation of anode current with grid voltage. This shows how small changes in the grid voltage produce large changes

Action of a capacitor.

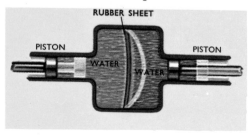

RUBBER SHEET

PISTON

PISTON

WATER

WATER

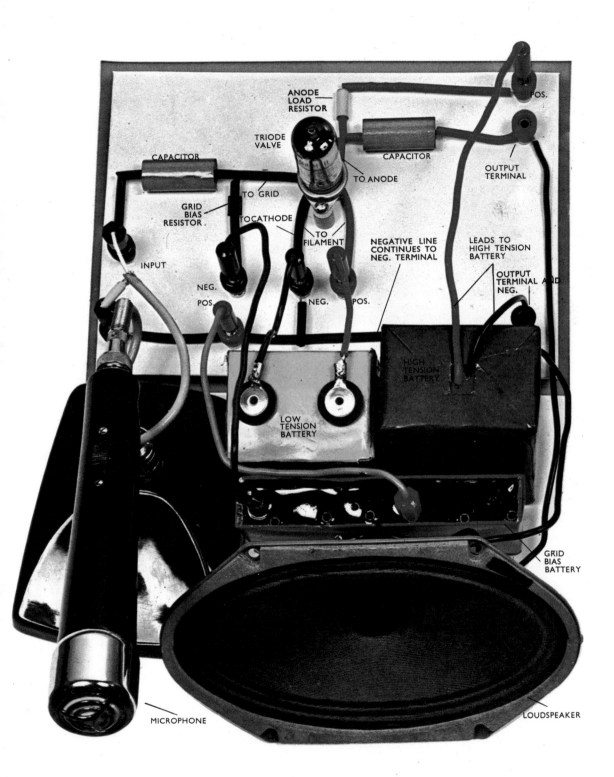

ANODE
LOAD
RESISTOR

TRIODE
VALVE

POS.

CAPACITOR

CAPACITOR

TO ANODE

OUTPUT
TERMINAL

TO GRID

GRID
BIAS
RESISTOR

TO CATHODE

INPUT

TO
FILAMENT

NEGATIVE LINE
CONTINUES TO
NEG. TERMINAL

LEADS TO
HIGH TENSION
BATTERY

OUTPUT
TERMINAL AND
NEG.

NEG.

POS.

NEG.

POS.

HIGH
TENSION
BATTERY

LOW
TENSION
BATTERY

GRID
BIAS
BATTERY

MICROPHONE

LOUDSPEAKER

19

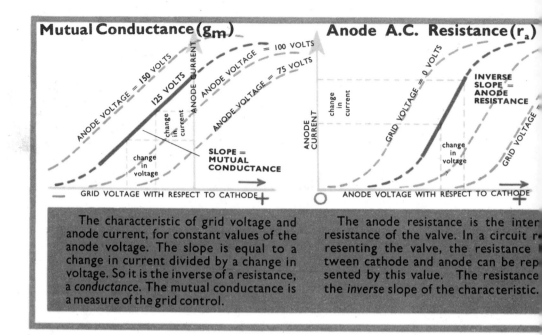

Mutual Conductance (g_m)

ANODE VOLTAGE = 150 VOLTS
125 VOLTS
ANODE VOLTAGE = 100 VOLTS
ANODE VOLTAGE = 75 VOLTS
ANODE CURRENT
change in current
change in voltage
SLOPE = MUTUAL CONDUCTANCE
GRID VOLTAGE WITH RESPECT TO CATHODE

Anode A.C. Resistance (r_a)

GRID VOLTAGE = 0 VOLTS
INVERSE SLOPE = ANODE RESISTANCE
ANODE CURRENT
change in current
change in voltage
GRID VOLTAGE
ANODE VOLTAGE WITH RESPECT TO CATHODE

The characteristic of grid voltage and anode current, for constant values of the anode voltage. The slope is equal to a change in current divided by a change in voltage. So it is the inverse of a resistance, a *conductance*. The mutual conductance is a measure of the grid control.

The anode resistance is the inter resistance of the valve. In a circuit r resenting the valve, the resistance tween cathode and anode can be rep sented by this value. The resistance the *inverse* slope of the characteristic.

in the anode current. The reading on the other voltmeter, the one reading *anode voltage*, is kept constant at, say, 75 volts.

In a typical triode valve, the anode current would start flowing when the grid voltage was about −2 volts. It would increase, as the grid voltage increased, to a maximum value, called the *saturation current*. When the results are plotted on a graph, the middle part of the line is straight, and the ends are curved. This is the typical form of a characteristic curve.

Then the anode voltage is changed to a slightly higher value−say 100 volts. The anode current starts to flow when the grid voltage is about −4 volts. It increases up to almost the same saturation current value, as the grid voltage is increased and made positive. This second characteristic curve is almost parallel to it over the straight portion.

The same procedure is carried out with anode voltages of 125 and 150 volts −and perhaps even higher values, depending on the type of triode valve under test. The result is a 'family' of characteristic curves.

The other set of characteristic curves is found in a similar experiment. This time the grid voltage is kept constant,

while the anode current and anode voltage vary. It involves adjusting the variable resistors in the circuit so that the voltmeter connected between the grid and the cathode always gives the same reading for one curve. Curves might be drawn for grid voltages of 0, −2, −4, −6 volts and so on.

The straight portion of the characteristic is the most useful part. Valves are usually operated so that their currents and voltages correspond to this part of the characteristic. Here the anode current is proportional to the grid voltage (on the first characteristic) and the anode current is proportional to the anode voltage (for a given grid voltage). This means that the valve amplifies all signals by the same amount−whether they are weak or strong signals; the ratio of output signal to input signal is constant.

Interpreting the Characteristics

Three important qualities associated with any triode valve are its *mutual conductance*, its *anode resistance* and its *amplification factor*. All these can be obtained from the straight portion of the characteristic curve. The mutual conductance is the slope of the first characteristic, and is a measure of the controlling

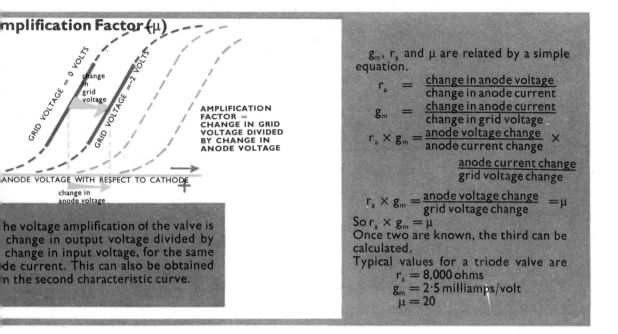

Amplification Factor (μ)

GRID VOLTAGE = 0 VOLTS

change in grid voltage

GRID VOLTAGE = 2 VOLTS

AMPLIFICATION FACTOR = CHANGE IN GRID VOLTAGE DIVIDED BY CHANGE IN ANODE VOLTAGE

ANODE VOLTAGE WITH RESPECT TO CATHODE

change in anode voltage

The voltage amplification of the valve is change in output voltage divided by change in input voltage, for the same anode current. This can also be obtained from the second characteristic curve.

g_m, r_a and μ are related by a simple equation.

$$r_a = \frac{\text{change in anode voltage}}{\text{change in anode current}}$$

$$g_m = \frac{\text{change in anode current}}{\text{change in grid voltage}}$$

$$r_a \times g_m = \frac{\text{anode voltage change}}{\text{anode current change}} \times \frac{\text{anode current change}}{\text{grid voltage change}}$$

$$r_a \times g_m = \frac{\text{anode voltage change}}{\text{grid voltage change}} = μ$$

So $r_a \times g_m = μ$

Once two are known, the third can be calculated.

Typical values for a triode valve are
$$r_a = 8{,}000 \text{ ohms}$$
$$g_m = 2 \cdot 5 \text{ milliamps/volt}$$
$$μ = 20$$

action of the grid. The anode resistance is obtained from the slope of the second characteristic. It is possible to use it to represent the output resistance of the valve in a circuit.

From all the meter readings, it would be possible to draw a third set of characteristics curves, showing anode voltage against grid voltage. The slope of the curve is the *amplification factor* of the valve. This can, however, be obtained from the other two characteristics.

CLASSES OF AMPLIFICATION

The grid of an electronic valve is a fine wire spiral encircling the cathode, and it is the controlling influence over the current flowing through the valve. It is nearer the cathode (the electron emitter) than the anode. A signal voltage of 2 or 3 volts applied to the grid has as much effect as a signal voltage of around 50 volts applied to the anode. The grid voltage varies by a small amount, and the anode voltage varies by a large amount. The grid is usually the input and the anode is part of the output circuit of the valve. The output signal is bigger than the input signal. The valve *amplifies*.

But the valve's output is not necessarily a perfect, enlarged replica of the input. Valves sometimes distort the signal.

The valve *characteristics* are two sets of curved lines (graphs) which show the variation of anode current with grid voltage, and anode current with anode voltage. Although the middle part of a triode valve's characteristic is practically straight, it curves at the ends. Over the straight portion, the output is proportional to the input, and the valve does not

Circuit diagram for plotting valve characteristics.

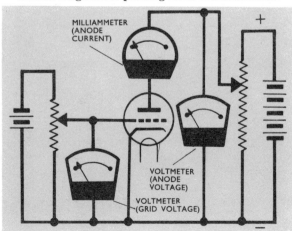

MILLIAMMETER (ANODE CURRENT)

VOLTMETER (ANODE VOLTAGE)

VOLTMETER (GRID VOLTAGE)

21

OUTPUT -
CLASS B WAVE

THESE CIRCUIT DIAGRAMS
INCLUDE ONLY THE
COMPONENTS NECESSARY
TO PASS ON THE
SIGNAL (THE A.C.
COMPONENTS). D.C.
COMPONENTS ARE
MISSING

INPUT WAVE-FORM

TRANSFORMER

OUTPUT -
CLASS B
WAVE

Class B push-pull

Each triode is biased at the cut-off voltage, so each can amplify only half the incoming signal. The signal is divided into two, amplified, and then joined again at the transformer. The result is a Class B push-pull amplifier. One valve deals with current pushes, and the other deals with current pulls.

A Class A amplifier. The incoming signal has a sine-wave form. The outgoing signal also has a sine-wave form.

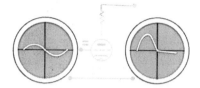

A Class B amplifier. The grid is more negative — it is biased just at the grid cut-off voltage. Half of the sine wave is practically undistorted. The other half does not appear at all in the output.

A Class C amplifier. The grid is even more negatively biased. The output is a series of distorted bursts, containing *harmonics* of the original sine-wave.

distort the signal. If the anode voltage and the grid voltage are set so that the valve operates over the curved portion of its characteristic, however, the signal becomes distorted.

The three ways of operating a valve over different parts of its characteristics are called *Classes A, B* and *C*.

Class A

A *Class A* valve amplifier is operated entirely in the straight portion. It produces a distortion-free output and is used as an audio-frequency amplifier. The one disadvantage is that the swing, to-and-fro, of the output voltage is restricted. The reason for this is that the valve is initially set with its grid voltage (grid *bias*) right in the middle of its specified values. This makes the valve operate in the middle of the straight portion of the characteristic curve.

During half of the signal cycle the grid voltage is greater than the bias voltage, and during the other half it is less. But the swing is still restricted to the straight part of the characteristic. The input swing is limited, so the output swing is also limited.

Class B

A *Class B* amplifier produces a large, undistorted swing in one direction, and then a very small, distorted swing in the other direction. A *single* Class B amplifier is little use as an audio-frequency amplifier, but a pair of valves, sharing the amplification of the signal so that one does one half and the other does the other half, can give a bigger output signal than a solitary Class A amplifier.

The grid of a Class B amplifier is biassed at its 'cutoff' voltage. At this voltage the grid cuts off the current flow from cathode to anode. Although the *anode* is at a positive voltage, relative to the cathode, and is attracting electrons away from the cathode, the electrons can be repelled *back* by a negative voltage on the *grid*.

At cutoff, no current flows. When the signal makes the grid even more negative than its cutoff voltage, no current can flow through the valve at all. The *anode* voltage does not change and this part of the signal does not appear at the valve output. When the signal added to the bias voltage makes the grid less negative, some current can flow. The valve is amplifying again, but can amplify only the positive parts of the signal.

But it is possible to connect a 'matched' pair of valves together so that each deals with half of the signal. One deals with the current pushes: the other with the current pulls. The result is a *Class B 'Push-Pull amplifier'*. Final stages of amplification in a radio set are often done by a Class B push-pull pair of valves (or transistors). They can give a bigger un-distorted output 'swing'.

Class C

The grid of a Class C amplifier is biassed even more negatively than it is in a Class B amplifier. The output is a series of short, sharp, highly distorted pulses. Nevertheless it can be used to amplify higher frequency signals (signals of *radio frequency*). The output signal is so highly distorted that, if it were analysed, it would be found to contain components of 2, 3, 4 or more times the frequency of the input signal. These, the *harmonics* of the fundamental frequency, can easily be dispensed with by *tuned* circuits.

Grid Current

The grid is always biassed negative with respect to the cathode of the valve. The grid should stay negative for the entire voltage swing. This is another limitation on the operating conditions of a valve. Should the grid become positive, it would attract electrons towards it. Electrons would leave the cathode-anode flow, and leave the valve through the grid as a *grid current*.

Grid current represents an unrecoverable loss, and a drain of energy away from the valve. It is also a source of additional distortion, since the partially-depleted anode current would not be a true reproduction of the input signal.

Part of the characteristic is a straight line. The maximum variation in the grid voltage, for completely undistorted output, is shown by the horizontal arrow. If the voltage swing is greater than this, it encroaches into the curved parts of the characteristic, and distortion may set in. The grid voltage is nearly always made *negative* (with respect to the cathode). If it is positive, it attracts some of the negatively-charged electrons, which would otherwise have gone to the anode. This produces an unwanted *grid current*.

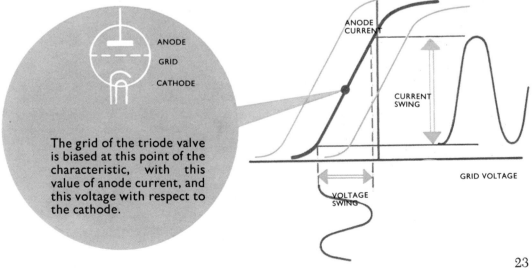

ANODE

GRID

CATHODE

The grid of the triode valve is biased at this point of the characteristic, with this value of anode current, and this voltage with respect to the cathode.

ANODE CURRENT

CURRENT SWING

GRID VOLTAGE

VOLTAGE SWING

Radio Receivers

IF THE SOUNDS coming from the loud-speaker of a radio receiver corresponded to all the broadcast signals falling on its aerial, the result would be an unintelligible jumble and the receiver would be completely useless. Any radio receiver must be able to select the signals from just one transmitter and reject all the others. In other words the receiver must be able to 'tune in' to one station at a time.

Most radio broadcasting stations send out 'electro-magnetic' radio waves of only *one* particular frequency and do not vary it (the varying frequencies of the microphone are conveyed with it by a method that does *not* change the frequency. This will be described on later pages). Unless broadcasting stations are so far from each other that they cannot interfere, no two stations should send out waves of the same frequency. The tuning of a radio receiver is simply a matter of making it respond more to radio waves of a particular frequency than to radio waves of any other frequency. When radio waves fall on an aerial they set up a current in much the same way as a current is set up in a coil when a magnet is moved close to it and the moving field of the magnet affects the coil. The current set up in the aerial is of precisely the same frequency as the waves themselves. This oscillating current causes electrons in the aerial circuit to surge backwards and forwards; in other words there is an *alternating* current in the aerial circuit. Actually every broadcast of every frequency will be received at the same time on the aerial and there will be an alternating current for each one. Each current has a different frequency and all of them conflict with each other. The backward electron surges of some frequencies reduce the forward electron surges of other frequencies or some frequencies may at some stage add their surges.

A circuit containing a coil and a capacitor will either reject or accept a current which alternates at one particular frequency. If the coil and capacitor are in *series* they provide an *easy* path for current of one particular frequency. If they are in *parallel* they provide a *difficult* path for current of one particular frequency and a comparatively easy path for currents of any other frequencies. It is rather like a fishing net that will hold in its mesh only fish of exactly the mesh size, small ones going through and larger ones bouncing by it. The frequency which is favoured depends upon the number of turns, diameter and type of core of the coil, and upon the area and separation of the plates of the capacitor and the material between them. By altering, say, the area of the capacitor's plates, the circuit can be made to favour current of a different frequency. In this way the tuned circuit can *resonate* at a particular frequency and can select just that current which corresponds to the broadcast signal which is wanted, out of the irregularly fluctuating surges of current in the aerial.

This process of selection, called *tuning*, may take place either after or before the signal is amplified by a valve. In the former case all the currents in the aerial circuit are amplified and the one required is picked out by a tuning circuit connected to the anode of the amplifying valve. In the latter case the required current is picked out by a tuning circuit and it alone is amplified. One circuit of each type is illustrated.

The first of the illustrations shows the tuning circuit connected to the anode of the amplifying valve. In this case the surges of electrons are fed to it from outside (i.e. from the anode). The arrangement is therefore a *parallel* or *rejector* circuit. It provides an easy path for currents of frequencies *other than the one to which the circuit is tuned*. The current rejected by the tuning circuit is given an alternative

24

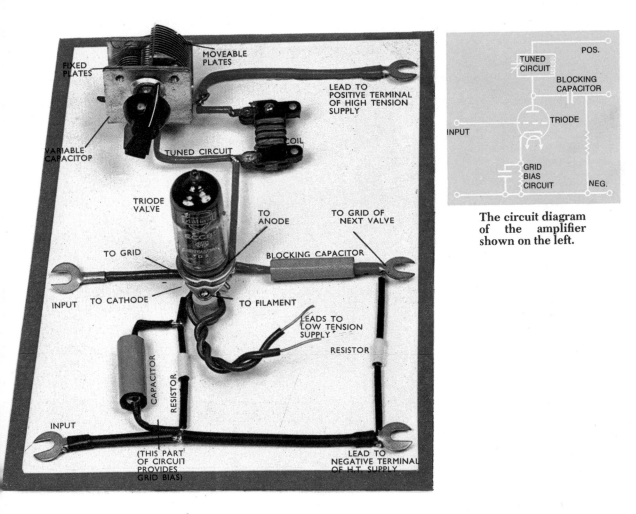

The circuit diagram of the amplifier shown on the left.

A triode amplifier incorporating a tuned anode circuit.

route leading (via a blocking capacitor which prevents the flow of direct current) to the grid of the next valve. All the other unwanted currents prefer to take the easy route provided by the tuning circuit so they do not arrive at the grid of the next valve.

The second of the illustrations (on page 26) shows the tuning circuit connected to the grid of an amplifying valve. In this particular case the aerial is not connected directly to the tuning circuit. Instead it is connected to a separate coil wound on the same core as the tuning coil. The two coils together form a transformer. Alternating currents in the aerial

coil produce a changing magnetic field which cuts through the tuning coil. The changing magnetic field in the tuning coil sets up voltages which cause electrons to surge backwards and forwards in the tuning circuit. Because the surges of electrons are set up *inside* the circuit and are not fed to it from outside, this arrangement is in fact a *series* or *acceptor* circuit. It provides an easy path for current of a particular frequency and a *large* current of that frequency will flow. Currents of other frequencies will also flow but they will be very weak. The voltage across the capacitor oscillates with precisely the same frequency as the large current in the tuning circuit. The voltage oscillations are fed to the grid of the valve for amplification.

THE RADIO-FREQUENCY STAGE

Radio waves falling on a suitable aerial set up fluctuating voltages. A radio receiver takes these fluctuating voltages, extracts the information they contain and delivers it as sound from a loudspeaker. The entire process is done in a number of steps and each step is usually performed by a separate 'stage' of the receiver. The first stage of a receiver, the radio-frequency stage, is concerned with amplifying the fluctuating voltages set up in the aerial.

The circuit illustrated on page 28 is designed to fulfil two functions. First it has to pick out signals of just one frequency. This function is called *tuning*. Secondly it has to amplify the signals which have

been selected, for the fluctuating voltages set up in the aerial are in most cases very weak.

The entire circuit consists of five parts. On the left is the *tuning circuit* containing two coils wound on the same hollow core. One end of the first coil (the aerial coil) is connected to the aerial and the other end is connected to the metal chassis on which all the components are mounted. This end of the coil is

The circuit diagram of the amplifier shown below.

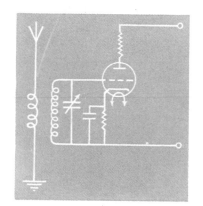

AERIAL

ANODE LOAD RESISTOR

TRIODE

AERIAL COIL

TUNING CIRCUIT

GRID BIAS CIRCUIT

A triode amplifier incorporating a tuned grid circuit.

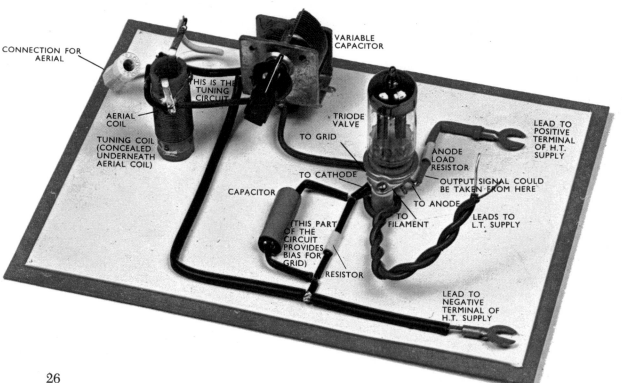

said to be 'earthed'. The two coils together make up a *transformer*. Surges of electrons in the aerial coil create a changing magnetic field which cuts through both the aerial coil and the tuning coil. Because the tuning coil is in a *changing* magnetic field, fluctuating voltages are set up in it just like those in the aerial. Electrons are forced to surge backwards and forwards by the fluctuating voltages. The electron surges are in fact alternating currents. Connected across the tuning coil is a very important component—the tuning capacitor. As the illustration shows, this has two sets of plates, one fixed and one moveable. By rotating one set of plates so that the areas which actually face each other are altered, the electrical size (capacitance) is altered. The circuit consisting of the tuning coil and the tuning capacitor provides an easy path for alternating currents of one particular frequency corresponding to the frequency of just one of the radio waves falling on the aerial. Any one frequency can be selected by altering the capacitance of the tuning capacitor, and a large current of this particular frequency flows around the tuning circuit. As the current alternates it puts first positive and then negative charges onto each set of plates of the tuning capacitor. Charges from one set of plates are fed straight to the control grid of the amplifying valve.

The valve used here is a *pentode*. It has five parts: a central cathode, a control grid, a screen grid, a suppressor grid, and around them all an anode. The functions of the cathode, control grid and anode are the same as those in the triode valve. The screen grid is designed to overcome a serious fault of the triode. In the triode the control grid (always negatively charged) and the anode (always positively charged) lying close together act as the two plates of a capacitor. If an actual capacitor were connected between the grid circuit and the anode circuit it would provide a very easy route for high frequency alternating currents. It could almost be regarded as a 'short circuit'; energy would 'leak' from the output (anode circuit) back to the input (grid circuit). This is roughly what happens in the triode. But if a loosely

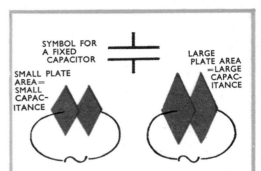

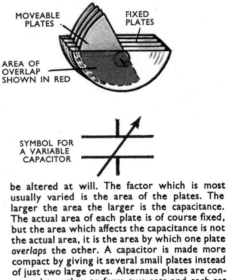

The *capacitance* of a capacitor is a measure of how much electrical charge can be stored on its plates. It is also a measure of the opposition ('capacitive reactance') which the capacitor offers to the passage of alternating currents of a given frequency. The capacitance depends upon three factors: (i) the areas of the plates, (ii) the distance between the plates and (iii) the type of material which lies between the plates. If any one of these factors is varied the capacitance will be altered. It is often necessary to have a *variable capacitor*—one whose capacitance can

be altered at will. The factor which is most usually varied is the area of the plates. The larger the area the larger is the capacitance. The actual area of each plate is of course fixed, but the area which affects the capacitance is not the actual area, it is the area by which one plate *overlaps* the other. A capacitor is made more compact by giving it several small plates instead of just two large ones. Alternate plates are connected together to form two sets and each set is insulated from the other. In a variable capacitor one set of plates is fixed while the other set is mounted on a spindle. When the spindle is turned the plates attached to it slide in and out of the fixed plates, thus the overlapping area alters and with it the capacitance.

wound wire spiral (a screen grid) placed between the control grid and the anode is given a fixed positive charge, usually less than that of the anode, it effectively cuts down the 'capacitor' effect of the anode and control grid.

The suppressor grid is designed to overcome another fault (which occurs

27

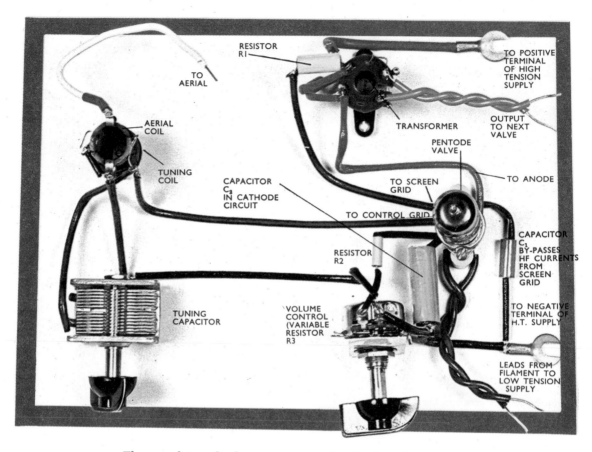

The complete radio-frequency stage of a simple radio receiver.

in triodes and diodes) called *secondary emission*. When an electron from the cathode hits the anode at speed it may knock several 'secondary' electrons out

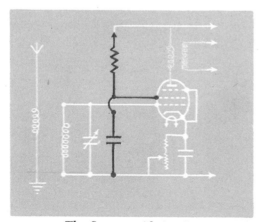

The Screen grid circuit.

of the anode itself. This is not serious in the triode, for the secondary electrons are repelled by the negatively charged control grid back to the positively charged anode. But having introduced a positively charged screen grid between the anode and the control grid this situation no longer holds good. Now the secondary electrons are *attracted* by the positively charged screen grid and therefore do not return to the anode. This flow of electrons, in opposition to the normal cathode-to-anode flow, is avoided by inserting next to the anode a third open wire spiral called the *suppressor grid*. Because this grid is connected to the cathode it is negatively charged and repels electrons. (*Note:* the suppressor grid is normally connected internally to the cathode, i.e. inside the valve envelope. In the illustration the connection is made by a wire hidden beneath the valve-holder.)

The electrons flowing out of the anode represent a current which fluctuates with the same frequency as the voltage variations on the grid. They are drawn towards the positive terminal of the high tension supply. In order to get there they must pass through one coil of a transformer. The fluctuating flow of electrons in the primary coil of the transformer produces an alternating voltage in the secondary. This alternating voltage has the same frequency as the alternating voltage put on the control grid of the pentode—but it is a very greatly increased alternating voltage. The output voltage from the transformer secondary may be taken to the grid of a second valve for further amplification.

The other components in the illustration are resistors and capacitors. Resistor R_1 is simply to drop the voltage of the high tension battery so that the screen grid is considerably less positive than the anode. Capacitor C_1 provides a route for any high frequency alternating currents which might occur in the screen grid circuit (i.e. if it acts as an anode) to pass to the chassis so that they do not affect any other part of the circuit.

The function of resistors R_2 and R_3 is to eliminate the need for a grid bias battery. The control grid must always be more negative than the cathode or distortion and waste of energy will result. In this amplifier, designed for use with a mains supply, it would be inconvenient and unreliable to have the necessary negative bias provided by a battery. Electrons flowing through the valve come from the negative terminal of the high tension (high voltage) supply. To arrive at the cathode they have to pass through the resistors R_2 and R_3. Since electrons flow from negative to positive this means that the cathode is more positive than the bottom end of R_3. In other words, the bottom end of R_3 is more negative than the cathode. The control grid is connected via the tuning circuit to the bottom end of R_3 (i.e. to the high tension negative line) and must therefore be more negative than the cathode. Thus the grid is made negative (compared with the cathode) without using a battery.

However, this method is not satisfactory as it stands because the flow of electrons to the cathode varies with the signal on the grid. When the signal is large the electron flow is large and the grid bias is therefore large too. When the signal is small the electron flow is small and the grid bias is small. The function of capacitor C_2 is to maintain a *steady* grid bias voltage. It allows *changes* in the flow of electrons to the cathode to by-pass R_2 and R_3. Thus there is only a *steady* flow of electrons through R_2 and R_3 and hence there must be a *steady* voltage across them.

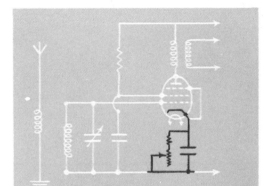

The cathode circuit provides a bias voltage for the control grid.

Resistor R_3 is a *variable* resistor. Its value can be adjusted merely by turning a knob which moves a sliding contact from one end of the resistor to the other. Because the sliding contact 'taps off' only a certain length of the resistor, only a fraction of its total resistance opposes the flow of electrons through it. A variable resistor is sometimes known as a rheostat—a Greek word meaning 'flow controller'. This is precisely what R_3 does—it controls the flow of electrons to the cathode and therefore governs the flow of electrons through the valve (the anode current). This rheostat is a most useful part of the amplifier, for, by making it possible to control the anode current, it acts as a volume control.

THE DIODE DETECTOR

The frequency of the sounds used in everyday speech varies between several hundred and about 15,000 cycles per second, and all people use approximately the same range of audio frequencies when they speak. If these sounds could be changed directly into radio waves and transmitted (and such low frequencies cannot in fact travel like radio waves), think what we would hear when we switched on a radio set. Not only could we get all the radio programmes of our own country but we should also hear everyone else who was transmitting wireless signals as well. We would get broadcasts from foreign countries, police signals, the messages from ships at sea and many other stations. This might seem to be a very good idea, but, unfortunately, all the different programmes would come through at the same time and the result would be a confused jumble of noise.

Fortunately, radio waves can have frequencies far higher than those we can hear (more than 50,000,000 cycles per second, in fact). The difficulty of taking ordinary sounds great distances by radio waves is overcome by using

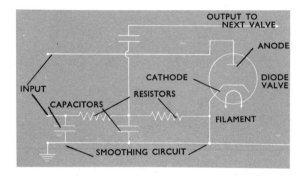

The detector stage of a simple radio receiver. The 'detection' (rectification) is carried out by a diode valve.

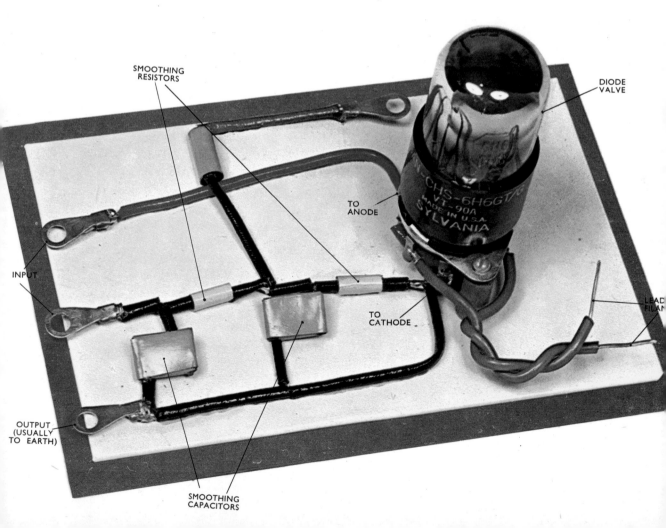

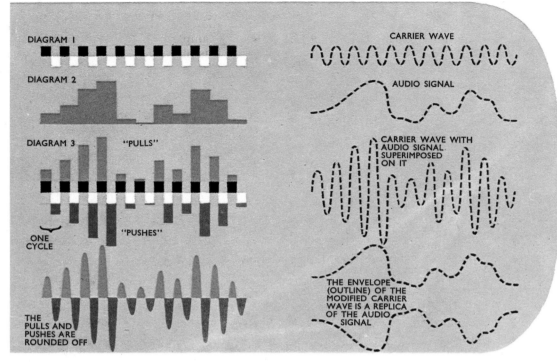

DIAGRAM 1

DIAGRAM 2

DIAGRAM 3   "PULLS"

ONE
CYCLE   "PUSHES"

THE
PULLS AND
PUSHES ARE
ROUNDED OFF

CARRIER WAVE

AUDIO SIGNAL

CARRIER WAVE WITH
AUDIO SIGNAL
SUPERIMPOSED
ON IT

THE ENVELOPE
(OUTLINE) OF THE
MODIFIED CARRIER
WAVE IS A REPLICA
OF THE AUDIO
SIGNAL

THE AUDIO FREQUENCY AND THE CARRIER FREQUENCY

A point to bear in mind about the usual kind of broadcast signals—amplitude-modulated (AM) signals: Audio (hearable) frequencies as such are NOT transmitted. What is transmitted is a fixed carrier (radio frequency which has a regular strength) (diagram 1). This, as it were, is the fixed ticking-over speed of a car engine. The audio signal is the *movement* of the car's accelerator. (2) Each cycle (pull-*and*-push) of the radio carrier frequency is given a different amount of throttle by the 'accelerator', and is made stronger according to how much pressure there is on the accelerator. (3) So each pair of pull-and-pushes (one cycle) of radio carrier frequency is made the same strength but either plus or minus. Successive cycles vary in strength according to the changes in the amount of 'throttle' administered by the audio signal. So the successive 'pull' pulses show a variation in strength that is the same pattern as the audio signal—and the 'push' pulses show an exact reverse image of the pattern.

Now the trouble with this transmitted radio frequency signal is that it just will NOT work a loudspeaker. Even if you could construct a speaker that could respond fast enough you could not hear it. Unfortunately the *overall* effect of the whole radio signal is zero, because each push cancels the movement obtainable from its paired 'pull'. This is why radio receivers need a detector stage to remove the 'push' pulses, so the overall effect is *not* zero.

radio waves of a *particular* frequency to carry the sound waves. This is done by taking the original audio frequency signal and imposing it on a much higher *carrier frequency* which is produced by an electronic device called an *oscillator*. As a result the *strength* of the carrier wave changes at the varying rate of the audio frequency.

A radio set is *tuned* to receive the *carrier frequency* (which is made different for different broadcasting stations), so now the set can pick up one programme at a time. To produce the original sound from the radio set the carrier frequency must be removed from the signal, leaving only the strength

variation as an effective electrical signal. This is the job of the *detector*. The simplest type of detector uses a *diode valve* and a *smoothing circuit*. The whole arrangement is called a *diode detector*. The job which the detector has to do is very similar to that of a rectifier. When the alternating current reaches the diode, the top parts of the wave shown in the diagram try to make the electrons move in one direction round the circuit while the bottom half of the wave tries to make them move in the opposite direction. But the electrons can only pass in one direction through the valve. Hence the diode removes the parts of the wave which try to make the

31

electrons pass from the anode to the cathode while the other parts of the wave get through unhindered.

In the detector the sizes of the inductors (coils) and capacitors in the filter section are different from those in a power rectifier (page 44) because the frequency of the pulses that have to be smoothed out is tremendously greater (maybe 20,000 times more frequent). The resulting wave has a pattern of variations that is the same as the original audio frequency signal. The action of the smoothing circuit causes one radio frequency pulse to run on into the next. As the strength of the pulses (their height on the graph) varies, the smoothing leaves the direct current *not* as a steady flow, but as a flow which varies in strength, though moving in one direction.

If two diodes are used arranged in exactly the same way as in the full-wave rectifier (see page 44) but with our new smoothing circuit, this will make the electron-flow out of the detector circuit nearly twice as great as in the half-wave detector described here.

By passing the transmitted wave through the diode detector it has been converted back into the original audio frequency form free from any interference from other broadcasting stations. It can then pass through the audio frequency amplifiers already described, where it is increased in strength enough to operate a loudspeaker.

The diode valve is literally a *valve*. It allows passage of electrons only ONE WAY. The pull-and-push of the radio signals between anode and cathode only *pulls* electrons from cathode to anode. Nothing happens, no electrons cross the valve, during the *'pushes'*, i.e. the negative half cycles. These little pictures of a pump with a hinged piston show an allegory of diode detection. Only when the handle is *pulled* will water come up and pour into the bucket. The down stroke merely bends the piston in two to act as a valve. The *strength* of each positive half cycle of signal will determine how much water gets into the bucket (i.e. how many electrons flow across the valve). The contents of successive odd-numbered buckets are the audio (hearable) frequency, which is the output of the diode—a flow of electrons varying in strength *in time with* the audio frequencies.

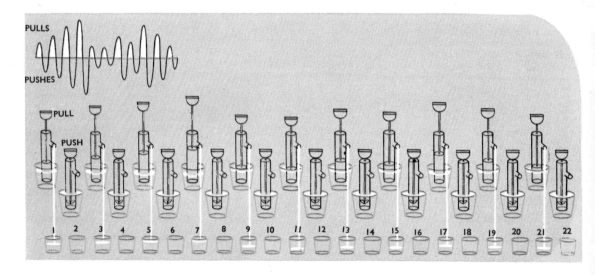

The one-way valve that turns the ineffective self-cancelling pull-and-push radio frequency into a varying audio signal that will work a loudspeaker.

HALF-WAVE DETECTION

Here we can trace the wave as it passes through the circuit as shown on a series of oscilloscopes. The Diode allows the electrons to go round the circuit in only one direction. Hence only a series of pulses passes into the smoothing circuit. In successive sections the electrons are slowed down slightly so that the pulses are drawn out and it is seen that the shape of the original audio frequency wave is returning. Another smoothing section smooths the wave out even more until the wave is indistinguishable from the original wave.

The circuit shown *below* is a simple half-wave rectifier. It consists of a diode valve, through which electrons can pass in only one direction (from cathode to anode) and a smoothing circuit to remove any 'ripple' still present in the one-way stream of electrons emerging from the valve. In this particular circuit the incoming current is fed to the cathode of the valve and the output is taken off from the anode. A negative voltage pulse arriving at the cathode from the input of the above circuit will drive electrons across the valve. These electrons will arrive eventually at point X and give it a negative charge. So in effect the negative voltage pulse has passed through the valve. A positive pulse cannot get through the valve since this would mean a flow of electrons from anode to cathode—a state of affairs which cannot occur.

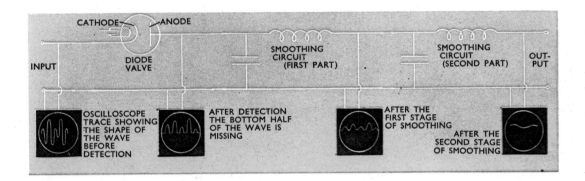

The circuit shown *below* is a diode detector. In this particular circuit the incoming signals are fed to the anode of the valve and the output is taken off from the cathode. A positive pulse arriving at the anode from the input will draw electrons from the cathode. The cathode in turn will draw electrons from point Y giving it a positive charge (i.e. a shortage of electrons). So in effect the positive voltage pulse has passed through the valve. A negative pulse cannot get through the valve. So the circuit on the right cuts off all the negative pulses whereas the circuit above cuts off all the positive pulses. In either case the effect is the same.

These two circuits differ in another obvious way: the rectifier above uses coils (inductors or chokes) in its smoothing circuit while the detector on the right uses resistors. For this purpose coils and resistors are virtually interchangeable. But resistors are preferable in the case of the detector simply because they are more compact and cheaper than coils—two important considerations in the design of a radio receiver.

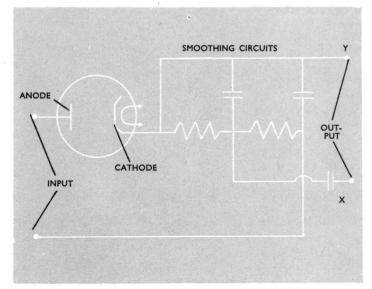

33

For the sake of clarity it will be supposed that just two radio waves are falling on an aerial. Each is carrying different information (called an audio signal) which is superimposed on the wave as a variation in strength. If a wave is shown on an oscilloscope screen it is apparent that the peaks of the waves are not all at the same level—the outline of the peaks is itself a wave and corresponds to the sound wave which originally fell on the microphone in the broadcasting studio. Each of the two radio waves has its own frequency. On the oscilloscope screen it is seen that the peaks are fairly widely spaced in one case (the wave from station

Many signals arrive at the aerial. Their combined effect is a jumble of irregularly shaped waves.

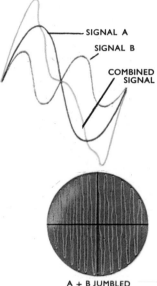

SIGNAL A
SIGNAL B
COMBINED SIGNAL

FROM STATION A

FROM STATION B

A + B JUMBLED ON AERIAL

CAPACITOR
COIL

TUNED CIRCUIT DIAGRAM

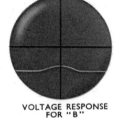

SIGNAL "A" SELECTED

VOLTAGE RESPONSE BEYOND TUNED CT. FOR "A"

VOLTAGE RESPONSE FOR "B"

To eliminate all signals other than the one wanted, a tuned circuit is set to resonate at this frequency.

AMPLIFYING THE SELECTED SIGNAL

IN AT THE GRID

OUT—AMPLIFIED—AT THE ANODE

A has a *medium* frequency) and closely packed together in another case (the wave from station B has a higher frequency). But the peaks in each wave are evenly spaced because the frequency of the basic radio wave (the 'carrier wave'

DETECTION

34

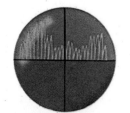

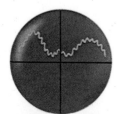

POSITIVE ½ CYCLES DETECTED BY 1st DIODE

NEGATIVE ½ CYCLES REVERSED & DETECTED BY 2nd DIODE

OUTPUT OF BOTH DIODES

"SMOOTHED" TOTAL EFFECT IS THE AUDIO SIGNAL ON THE MICROPHONE AT STATION A

upon which the audio signal is superimposed) from each of the transmitting stations is fixed.

These two radio waves set up two alternating voltages in the aerial. The two voltages, however, immediately add themselves together to give a very complicated combined voltage in which the individual signals seem to be completely lost. However, all signals other than the one required can be removed using a tuned circuit. A parallel tuned circuit is set to resonate at the frequency of the required signal, and the frequency can be altered by turning the knob of the capacitor in the tuning circuit.

A SIMPLE RADIO RECEIVER

It has been explained how electrical oscillations of both audio and radio frequencies are amplified by suitable electronic circuits and also how a radio wave can be detected, i.e. how the high-frequency carrier wave is removed from the radio signal, leaving the audio frequency signal to be changed into sound. The radio frequency and audio frequency amplifiers and the detector can be thought of as building blocks in a radio circuit.

We are now able to see how these various blocks, called *stages*, all joined together. Each stage has a definite function to perform in changing the radio signal, which is picked up by the aerial, back into a sound very similar to that which was made in the broadcasting studio. The working of a complete radio receiver can be understood by looking at a block diagram in which each stage is drawn simply as a 'block'. (The aerial and earphones are shown as symbols because they can be drawn so simply.)

Looking at the block diagram of the simple radio receiver we see that the first thing that is needed is the *aerial*. The aerials on modern receivers are usually inside the set, but everyone will be familiar with the radio aerial on, for example, a car. An aerial is simply a metal strip, either a rod or a wire. When the radio wave reaches an aerial it causes electrons in the rod to move in time with

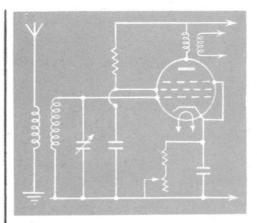

THE AERIAL, THE TUNER, AND THE RADIO FREQUENCY AMPLIFYING CIRCUIT.

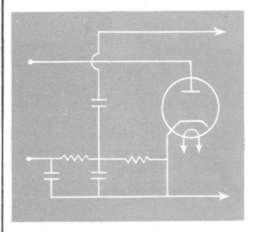

THE DIODE DETECTOR STAGE OF THE CIRCUIT. THE DETECTED OUTPUT IS TAKEN FROM THE CATHODE.

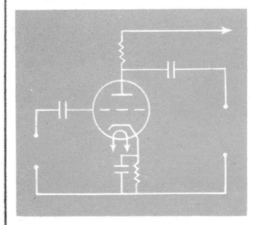

THE AMPLIFICATION OF THE OUTPUT FROM THE DETECTOR. THIS IS THE AUDIO FREQUENCY AMPLIFIER. THIS CIRCUIT HAS NORMAL POWER SUPPLIES, AND THE BIAS VOLTAGE IN THE CATHODE CIRCUIT IS AS DESCRIBED ON PAGE 29.

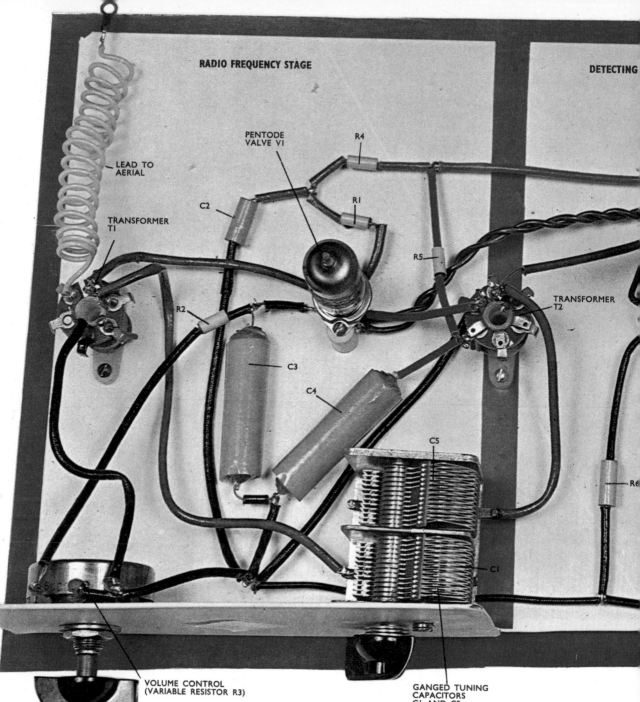

PENTODE
VALVE VI

R4

R1

LEAD TO
AERIAL

C2

R5

TRANSFORMER
TI

TRANSFORMER
T2

R2

C3

C4

C5

CI

R6

VOLUME CONTROL
(VARIABLE RESISTOR R3)

GANGED TUNING
CAPACITORS
CI AND C5

the wave. Hence the aerial converts the radio signal into a movement of electrons, i.e. into a varying electric current.

There are many radio signals being broadcast all the time, so the next requirement of the receiver is a device to remove all the signals except the one that we want to listen to. In terms of a radio set, we require one carrier signal to get through and all the others to be stopped. It has been explained how this is done using a *parallel tuned circuit* which allows only the frequency at which the circuit is set to resonate to pass and stops other frequencies. Since a tuned circuit is used this stage is called a *tuner*. To change the programme which is heard from the set the resonant

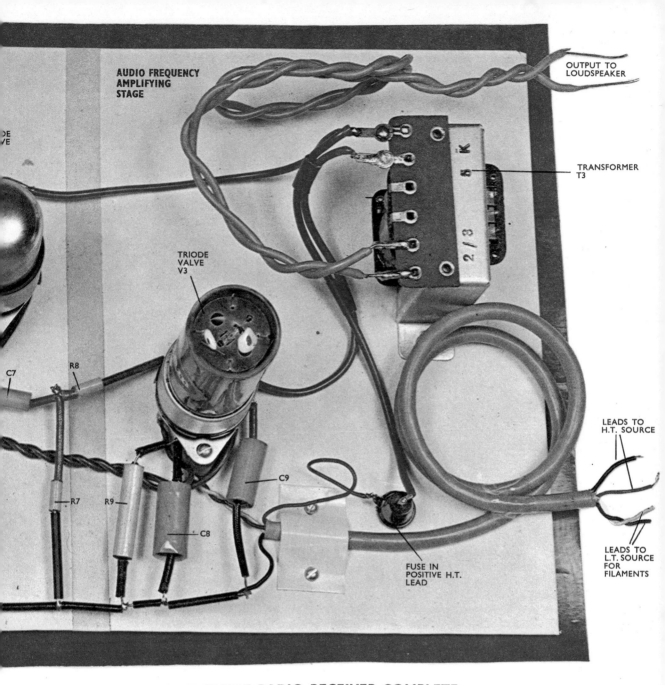

AUDIO FREQUENCY
AMPLIFYING
STAGE

OUTPUT TO
LOUDSPEAKER

TRANSFORMER
T3

TRIODE
VALVE
V3

C7

R8

C9

R7

R9

C8

FUSE IN
POSITIVE H.T.
LEAD

LEADS TO
H.T. SOURCE

LEADS TO
L.T. SOURCE
FOR
FILAMENTS

THE SIMPLE RADIO RECEIVER COMPLETE

frequency of the tuner is changed. This is most conveniently done by changing the capacitance of the tuned circuit, so a variable capacitor is put into this part of the circuit.

Coming from the tuner is a single radio frequency signal which contains the audio signal that we want to listen to. Since the voltage variation in the aerial is very small, the signal will be weak. Hence the next stage in the circuit is an *amplifier*. This amplifier must be able to work at the high frequency of the carrier wave, so a pentode (five electrode) valve is used instead of a triode. The size of the signal from the pentode can be very conveniently regulated by a variable resistor connected between the

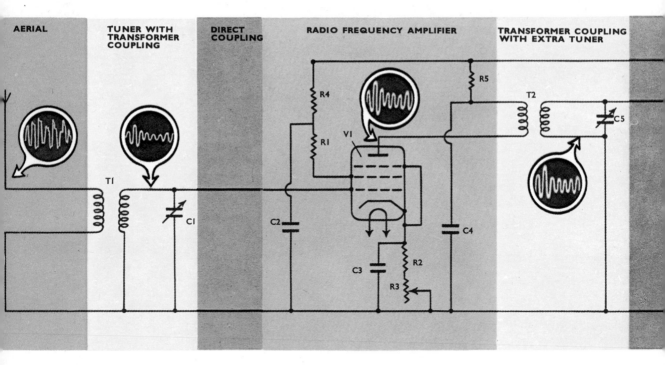

AERIAL

TUNER WITH
TRANSFORMER
COUPLING

DIRECT
COUPLING

RADIO FREQUENCY AMPLIFIER

TRANSFORMER COUPLING
WITH EXTRA TUNER

cathode and the 'earth', so a variable resistor connected here is used as the volume control for the set (since the size of the signal passed through the set is proportional to the amount of sound which comes out of the loudspeaker).

The output from the radio frequency amplifier is a *large modulated oscillation*. The *modulation* is now removed using a *diode detector*. The oscillation coming from the detector is the original audio frequency signal.

An audio frequency oscillation is turned into sound by passing it into ear-phones or into a loudspeaker. However, a lot of power is needed to create audible sound in the loudspeaker. For this reason an audio frequency amplifier stage is put in after the detector. This increases the size of the signal which may now be heard when a pair of earphones are con-nected. A loudspeaker requires more power to work it than earphones, so if the radio is required to work with a loud-speaker another audio frequency am-plifier should be added to this stage.

Since the amplifiers make the signal bigger, i.e. supply power to the signal, they, themselves, need a source of power.

In this receiver the power comes from the normal household mains supply which is turned into a steady direct cur-rent by passing it through a *rectifier* The rectifier is then connected to the terminals marked H.T.+ and H.T.− on the circuit diagram. Normally the rec-tifier would be built into the receiver; here it has been kept separate in order to simplify the circuit.

It should now be possible to see how the electronic circuits which make up the different stages are *coupled* together to form the complete circuit. There are three types of coupling called *trans-former coupling*, *resistance-capacitance coupling*, and *direct coupling*. Which of these is chosen to connect one stage to the next depends upon the signal which is passing. The transformer coupling can be used as an extra tuning stage, since the coils of the transformer can be made part of tuned circuits (which allow only one frequency to pass). This is useful in coupling the radio frequency stage to the diode detector, since the signal which passes must have only one frequency, the frequency of the carrier wave. To change the frequency of the carrier wave

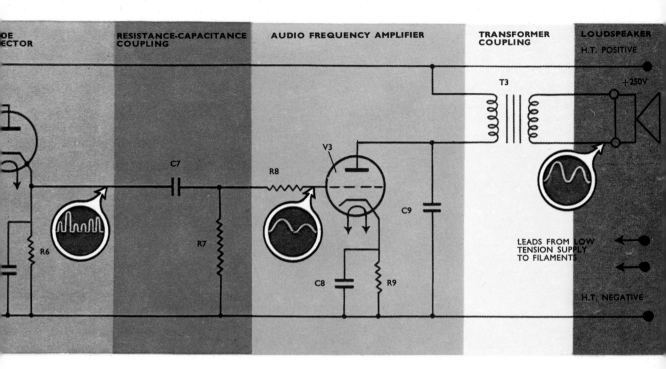

which is allowed through in order to change the programme, therefore, *both* of the variable capacitors must be adjusted. For this reason the controls of the capacitors are joined together inside the set. They are said to be *ganged*.

The audio signal which is left after detection is only a single frequency if the note of a tuning fork is being broadcast. Any more complicated sound, such as an instrument or a voice, will consist of a mixture of various audio frequencies and the signal will not have a *regular* shape. Accordingly all sounds within the audio range of frequencies must be passed to the earphones, for the value of the capacitor can be chosen to allow all wanted frequencies through. Hence a resistance-capacitance coupling is used in the output from the audio frequency amplifier stage (where all frequencies up to about 15,000 cycles per second may be present).

Finally *direct coupling* is the name given when the output from one stage is fed directly into the input of the next. This is the obvious way to couple circuits. Direct coupling is not always used because the following stage of the cir-

cuit would not be protected from a large steady voltage if it suddenly appeared, caused, perhaps, by a *short* to the H.T. line. As the circuit diagram shows, the H.T. line is not connected to the tuner, so there is no chance of a large voltage getting to the pentode from this. Hence direct coupling is used between the tuner and the radio frequency amplification stage.

The circuit looks very complicated to begin with but, remembering what the circuit diagram of each stage looks like, it should soon become clear. The amplifying stages look simpler in the complete circuit diagram since amplifiers, which need to be connected to a power supply as shown in the block diagram, are all connected to the same power line. Hence all their anodes are joined to the same high tension line (through suitable resistances which ensure that the valve is working under the best conditions for it), while all the valve cathodes are led through bias resistors to the same earth line.

The circuit which has been described contains all the stages which are essential for a receiver, but the modern domestic receiver is normally rather more complicated. This takes the form of a super-heterodyne (superhet) receiver, to be described next.

THE SUPERHET RADIO RECEIVER

In the early days of radio when there were few transmitters the carrier frequencies used for the different programmes could be made very different from one another. Hence, even when the simple radio receiver was used, the programmes could be separated from one another by the set and good-quality reception obtained. However, as time went on, more and more programmes were transmitted. This meant that more carrier frequencies had to be fitted into the same possible range of transmitting frequencies.

It then becomes necessary to use more selective methods to separate out the required carrier frequency from all the unwanted ones. It was found that a simple tuned circuit (capacitor and coil) becomes more selective as the frequency of the carrier wave is decreased. For this reason it is possible to make the receiver more sensitive by reducing the frequency of the carrier signals after they have entered the set. The carrier frequency, once it has been lowered, is known as the *intermediate frequency,* and a set which uses this method for gaining increased selectivity is known as a *super-heterodyne radio receiver.*

In order to convert the simple radio receiver into a superhet receiver it is necessary to add stages which will lower the carrier frequencies. This may be done by passing the carrier frequency through a *mixer* into which a 'local oscillator' is also passing a constant frequency. This is the heterodyne principle. Hence the new block diagram for the superhet receiver is seen to be the same as for the simple radio receiver except for the mixer (which also has an oscillator connected to it) and an amplifier all placed between the radio frequency amplifier and the detector.

It is not always necessary to make each stage of a set completely separate with a different valve for each stage. Usually one valve can be made to do two jobs, which means that the set can be made more cheaply and also can be made smaller. In most commercially-built superhets the local oscillator valve and the mixer valve are contained in the same envelope. The composite valve is then known as a 'frequency changer'. But here, for clarity, each stage has been laid out as a separate unit.

The mixer is simply a pentode valve with the radio signal fed (after tuning) to its first grid, and the local oscillations fed to its third output grid. The signals taken from the anode include the *intermediate frequency.* The local oscillations and the original radio signal will also appear at the anode, but since the intermediate frequency is always lower than either of these it is easily separated from them (and from the changed frequencies of all the other signals which were picked up by the aerial) by a capacitor-and-coil circuit. This circuit is really part of a transformer which couples the mixer stage to the intermediate frequency amplifier stage. It is tuned to one definite frequency — usually 465 kc/s (465,000 cycles per second). This may seem strange since the receiver must be able to pick up a wide range of carrier waves. The explanation is that the main tuning capacitor is 'ganged' with the variable capacitor in the local oscillator circuit and the two move together. Suppose the incoming carrier wave has a frequency of 600 kc/s. In this case the local oscillations have a frequency of 1065 kc/s and the intermediate frequency will be $(1065-600)=465$ kc/s. If now the receiver is retuned to accept a carrier wave of 800 kc/s, the setting of the tuning capacitor has to be altered. This adjustment not only affects the tuning capacitor, it automatically adjusts the local oscillator until its output frequency is 1265 kc/s. The intermediate frequency will be $(1265-800)=465$ kc/s, i.e. the same as it was before.

Both the primary and the secondary windings of the coupling transformer are tuned to the intermediate (465 kc/s) frequency to make doubly sure that all

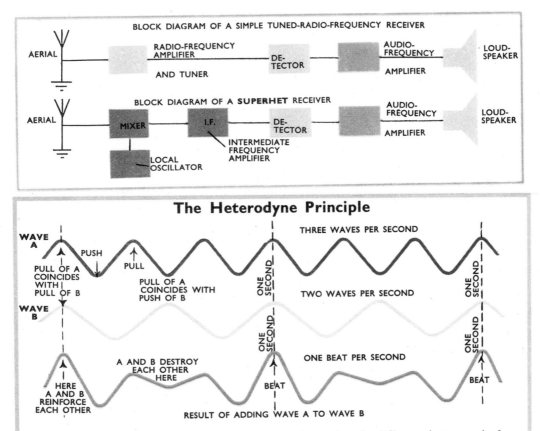

BLOCK DIAGRAM OF A SIMPLE TUNED-RADIO-FREQUENCY RECEIVER

AERIAL — RADIO-FREQUENCY AMPLIFIER AND TUNER — DE-TECTOR — AUDIO-FREQUENCY AMPLIFIER — LOUD-SPEAKER

BLOCK DIAGRAM OF A SUPERHET RECEIVER

AERIAL — MIXER — I.F. INTERMEDIATE FREQUENCY AMPLIFIER — DE-TECTOR — AUDIO-FREQUENCY AMPLIFIER — LOUD-SPEAKER

LOCAL OSCILLATOR

The Heterodyne Principle

WAVE A — THREE WAVES PER SECOND — PUSH — PULL — PULL OF A COINCIDES WITH PULL OF B — PULL OF A COINCIDES WITH PUSH OF B — ONE SECOND — ONE SECOND

WAVE B — TWO WAVES PER SECOND — ONE SECOND

A AND B DESTROY EACH OTHER HERE — ONE BEAT PER SECOND — HERE A AND B REINFORCE EACH OTHER — BEAT — BEAT

RESULT OF ADDING WAVE A TO WAVE B

If two keys close together on a piano are struck simultaneously the sound produced rises and falls to give a throbbing effect. The same effect is often heard with a twin-engined aircraft when the engines are running at slightly different speeds. The reason for this throbbing (or 'beating' as it is called) is that sound travels through the air as a series of 'pushes' and 'pulls'. If the 'pulls' of one note coincide with the 'pulls' of another note the two notes reinforce each other and a loud sound is heard. But if the 'pulls' of the first note coincide with the 'pushes' of the second the two notes tend to cancel each other and only a faint sound is heard. When the notes are of different frequencies 'pulls' of the first cannot coincide with every 'pull' of the second, since they are bound to occur at different intervals. However, the 'pulls' and 'pushes' of the note with the higher frequency do catch up with the less frequent 'pulls' and 'pushes' of the other note from time to time, and when they coincide exactly an increase in loudness results—hence the throbbing effect. The number of throbs or beats which occur in one second is equal to the *difference* between the frequencies of the two notes (see diagram).

Just as two sounds will interfere with each other to produce beat notes, so two alternating voltages (which can be thought of as a series of 'pulls' and 'pushes') mixed together will produce a similar effect. The resulting voltage alternates with a frequency equal to the difference between the frequencies of the two original voltages. Thus if a voltage alternating at 500 cycles per second is mixed with a voltage alternating at 1500 cycles per second the resulting voltage will rise and fall 1000 times per second. This is the principle of 'heterodyning'. If the resulting frequency is outside the audible range the principle is called 'supersonic heterodyning' and a radio receiver employing the principle is called a *superhet* for short. A radio signal can be used in place of either of the alternating voltages. The voltage which results from the mixing will have a lower frequency than the radio signal but it will still carry the same information that had been superimposed on the original radio signal.

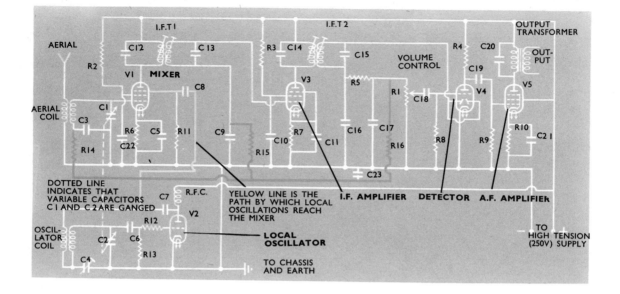

The model on the page opposite is an actual *superhet receiver*. It has been laid out to correspond as far as possible with the circuit diagram shown above. A practicable layout would be very different. For clarity the power supply components have been omitted. The line shown in green is part of an *automatic volume control system* which has not yet been described.

Note that the two intermediate frequency transformers (I.F.T.1 and I.F.T.2) are contained in aluminium screening cans which conceal the capacitors fixed across each primary and each secondary. Since these capacitors are fixed, the transformers are tuned to 465 kc/s by screwing an iron dust-core in and out of the coils, thus altering the inductance of the coils.

the unwanted frequencies are removed. The oscillation is then passed into an amplifier, called the *intermediate frequency amplifier*, to make sure that the oscillations are large enough to work the diode detector. The intermediate frequency amplifier is exactly the same as the radio frequency amplifier (described on page 26) since, of course, the intermediate frequency is still a radio frequency (but a rather lower one).

The superhet arrangement is particularly good since, although the quality of the sound which it produces is very much better than that of the simple radio receiver, the controls are no more difficult to set than in the simple receiver case. To vary the frequency of the carrier frequency allowed through the set, it is the frequency of the oscilla-

tor and not of the tuned circuits (other than the first) which is changed in the superhet arrangement. This can be done by varying the positions of the plates of the capacitor in the tuned part of the local oscillator. The mixer has the effect of changing the audio frequency modulation from the carrier frequency to the intermediate frequency which alone can pass through the tuned selector circuits. Since the intermediate frequency is kept constant, in order to select another programme it is necessary only to vary the oscillator frequency until the difference between it and the new required carrier frequency is again the intermediate frequency. Hence only one frequency control is necessary. The volume control is the same as that used for the simple radio receiver.

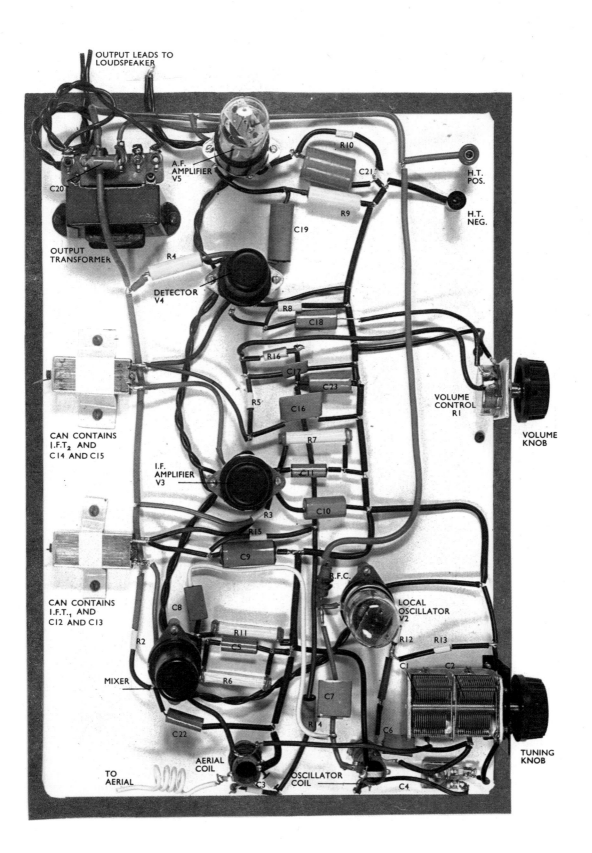

OUTPUT LEADS TO
LOUDSPEAKER

A.F.
AMPLIFIER
V5

R10

C21

H.T.
POS.

R9

H.T.
NEG.

C20

C19

OUTPUT
TRANSFORMER

R4

DETECTOR
V4

R8

C18

R16

C17

C23

VOLUME
CONTROL
R1

VOLUME
KNOB

R5

C16

CAN CONTAINS
I.F.T₂ AND
C14 AND C15

R7

I.F.
AMPLIFIER
V3

C11

R3

C10

R15

C9

CAN CONTAINS
I.F.T₁ AND
C12 AND C13

R.F.C.

C8

LOCAL
OSCILLATOR
V2

R2

R11

R12

R13

C5

C1

C2

MIXER

R6

TUNING
KNOB

C7

C22

R14

C6

TO
AERIAL

AERIAL
COIL

OSCILLATOR
COIL

C3

C4

43

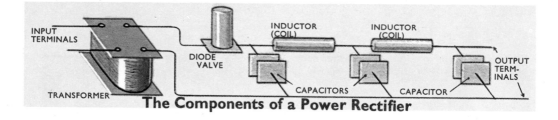

The Components of a Power Rectifier

Power Rectifiers

THE POWER from electricity can be used in many ways: it can be used to drive electric trains, to produce light in an electric light bulb, to boil water in an electric kettle or to provide power to work an electric component such as an amplifier.

Electric power may be obtained either from a generator or from a battery. There is, however, a difference between the electricity produced from these two sources. Current from the battery flows steadily in one direction (direct current) but, because of the way in which it is produced, the current from the generator comes in bursts. It is this latter type of electricity which we get in our homes and, because the current flows first in one direction and then in the opposite direction, it is called *alternating current*.

This alternation does not matter when the current is being used to produce heat or light but, when it is needed to provide power for electronic apparatus, steady *direct current* is usually necessary. Batteries could be used to provide this but they last for only a limited time,

are expensive, and cannot easily give high voltages which are often needed. For these reasons alternating current from the mains is used whenever possible as a source of electric power. Then, if direct current is needed, the alternations are directed one way. This is done by a device called a *rectifier*.

The simplest type of valve rectifier consists of a diode valve, a capacitor and some *smoothing sections*. The circuit model on the following page shows a rectifier as it might appear in a radio or television set. However, it is possible to understand how it works only by looking at the circuit diagram. The alternating current is fed into the diode through a transformer. This transformer is not essential to the working of the rectifier, but it may be used to make sure that the current coming into the valve is of the correct size—not too large to damage it. Hence the transformer is always included in practice. Only the *size* of the current changes in the transformer. The *shape* of the wave does not change, as can be seen if it is displayed on the screen of an oscilloscope.

A FULL-WAVE RECTIFIER

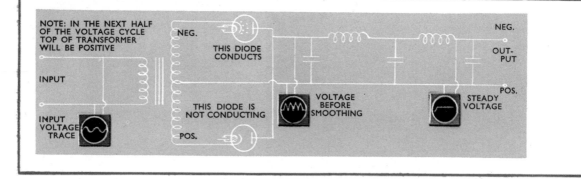

HALF-WAVE RECTIFIER

The shape of the voltage 'wave' at different parts of the circuit shown on an oscilloscope screen.

(Above) At this instant electrons pass across the diode because point X is experiencing the negative half of the voltage cycle and so the cathode is more negative than the anode.

In the next half of the voltage cycle point X is positive and no electrons flow since the cathode is now more positive than the anode. If the *anode* had been connected to the transformer (as is the case in the circuit described in the text) then electrons would flow during the positive halves of the voltage cycle.

SMOOTHING

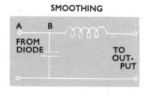

The action of the *smoothing section*. When the pulse arrives at B some electrons pass on through the inductor and some charge the capacitor. When the pulse dies away the capacitor starts to discharge again and since electrons cannot return through the valve at A they must pass through the inductor. The capacitor takes a longer time to discharge the electrons than it does to receive them in being charged. The size of the capacitor is chosen so that it is only partly discharged before the next pulse arrives. Hence instead of the series of pulses, we have only a ripple in the voltage coming from the smoothing section.

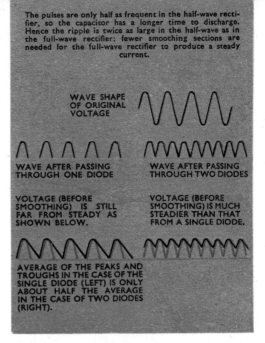

The pulses are only half as frequent in the half-wave rectifier, so the capacitor has a longer time to discharge. Hence the ripple is twice as large in the half-wave as in the full-wave rectifier; fewer smoothing sections are needed for the full-wave rectifier to produce a steady current.

WAVE SHAPE OF ORIGINAL VOLTAGE

WAVE AFTER PASSING THROUGH ONE DIODE

WAVE AFTER PASSING THROUGH TWO DIODES

VOLTAGE (BEFORE SMOOTHING) IS STILL FAR FROM STEADY AS SHOWN BELOW.

VOLTAGE (BEFORE SMOOTHING) IS MUCH STEADIER THAN THAT FROM A SINGLE DIODE.

AVERAGE OF THE PEAKS AND TROUGHS IN THE CASE OF THE SINGLE DIODE (LEFT) IS ONLY ABOUT HALF THE AVERAGE IN THE CASE OF TWO DIODES (RIGHT).

TO COMPARE THE EFFECT OF THE HALF-WAVE AND THE FULL-WAVE RECTIFIERS

The chapter on the diode explained that electrons can pass through the valve in *only one direction*. Current can flow through the valve circuit only when the anode is at a higher voltage (i.e. more positive) than the cathode. This occurs in the positive half of the wave-cycle. In the negative half the anode is at a lower voltage (i.e. more negative) than the cathode and the flow of electrons stops. The current in the valve circuit is a series of *pulses*. It has the same form as the original A.C. voltage but the negative parts have been completely cut off.

The pulses which remain can now be made into a steady current using a smoothing circuit which consists of pairs of coils (called inductors) and capaci-

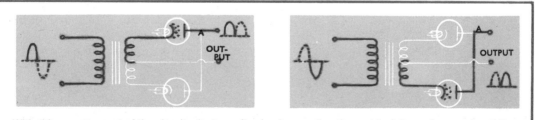

With this arrangement of the circuit, electrons flowing in one direction get to A through one valve. If they flow in the other direction they get *to the same place, A, again*, through the other valve. The pulse reaching A *each time is exactly the same whichever valve it has come through*. Hence the effect of the valves is to change the alternating current into a series of pulses all in the same direction as can be seen from the oscilloscope screen attached to the circuit.

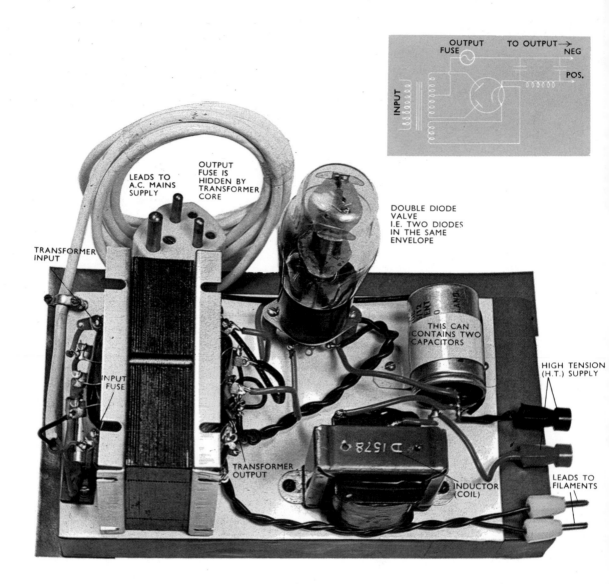

OUTPUT FUSE

TO OUTPUT → NEG

POS.

INPUT

LEADS TO A.C. MAINS SUPPLY

OUTPUT FUSE IS HIDDEN BY TRANSFORMER CORE

DOUBLE DIODE VALVE I.E. TWO DIODES IN THE SAME ENVELOPE

TRANSFORMER INPUT

THIS CAN CONTAINS TWO CAPACITORS

HIGH TENSION (H.T.) SUPPLY

INPUT FUSE

TRANSFORMER OUTPUT

INDUCTOR (COIL)

LEADS TO FILAMENTS

tors arranged as shown in the diagrams. The *ripple* will not be completely removed after it is passed across one inductor-capacitor pair but the smoothing may be improved by adding more pairs joined on in the same way as the first. It is possible to make the ripple so small that the current coming from the rectifier is effectively direct current. Since only half the wave is used to produce the steady current this arrangement is known as a *half-wave rectifier*.

The *full-wave* rectifier makes use of all the wave. This rectifier works on the same principle as the half-wave type just described but it has two diodes arranged so that, when the first valve stops passing current, the electrons can pass through the second. This is shown in the circuit diagram with a smoothing circuit joined on as before.

With the full-wave rectifier fewer sections are needed in the filter unit (smoothing unit) because the closer pulses tend to make a more even voltage. Also the electron flow from the output terminals is twice the flow which would have been obtained from the half-wave rectifier.

46

Oscillatory Circuits

PREVIOUS CHAPTERS have described how a radio valve can be used as an amplifier and as a rectifier or detector. There is a third and very important application of the radio valve—namely in the production of rapidly alternating currents. In a radio transmitter rapidly alternating currents are fed (indirectly) to the aerials to produce the carrier waves which travel out to the receiving aerials. These alternating currents are simply to-and-fro movements, or *oscillations*, of electrons. The circuits which generate them are called *oscillators*. The oscillations are actually produced in a *resonant tuned circuit* consisting simply

of an inductor (coil) and a capacitor. The capacitor stores electrons, and when the inductor is connected across it, the stored electrons surge from one plate to the other. But having reached the other plate the electrons surge back again and the whole process repeats over and over at regular intervals. Thus, once the capacitor has been charged and the coil connected across it, electrons surge backwards and forwards around the circuit. Each complete forward and backward surge makes up one oscillation. The number of oscillations taking place in one second is called the frequency, and depends upon the sizes of the

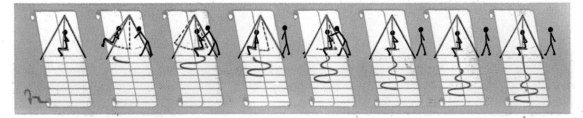

When the swing is set in motion and then left, its to-and-fro motion gets smaller and smaller until it stops. This is shown clearly if the swing traces out its own path on a roll of paper moving at right angles to the swing.

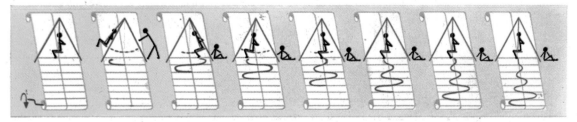

The same swing and the same moving roll of paper. This time the trace does not 'tail-off' because the swing is given a series of pushes to make each to-and-fro movement as big as the one before it.

This time the pushes are given at the 'wrong' moment and the swing is quickly brought to a standstill.

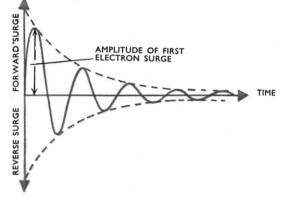

(*Left*) A capacitor is connected to a battery: atoms in one set of plates acquire surplus electrons while atoms in the other set lose electrons. (*Right*) The battery is replaced by a coil: surplus electrons surge through coil to make good deficit on opposite plates.

So many electrons arrive that plates which had electron deficit now have surplus. Charges on plates have been reversed so electrons surge back in opposite direction. (*Below*) Graph below shows how successive surges decrease in size.

capacitor and the inductor. Adjusting the size of the capacitor or the size of the inductor (not as easy to alter as the capacitor in practice) alters the frequency of the oscillations.

In some ways electrical oscillations are comparable to the swings of a pendulum: the electrons surge backwards and forwards, the pendulum swings to-and-fro. Normally, when a pendulum is set in motion its swings get smaller and smaller in amplitude (distance from mid-point to furthest point of a swing). The energy given to the pendulum at the start is lost in overcoming friction and is eventually turned into heat. The time taken for each gradually shortening swing nevertheless remains the same. In other words the *frequency* is constant. This is also true of the electrical oscillations set up in a tuned circuit. In each oscillation some electrical energy is turned into heat in overcoming the resistance which the circuit is bound to

offer to the flow of electrons. As the energy is used up the oscillations get smaller and smaller in amplitude (i.e. the peak value of each surge is less than that of the preceding surge). The frequency, however, remains the same. Obviously the oscillations set up by a surge of electrons in a simple tuned circuit are of little practical value if they quickly die away to nothing. A pendulum would be of little value in a clock if its swings died away to nothing. But in a clock the pendulum swings do not die

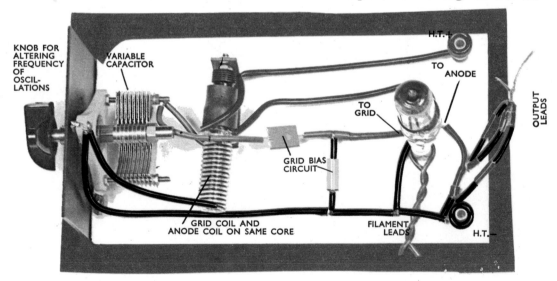

away because the energy lost in overcoming friction is replaced by energy stored in the mainspring (or in a falling weight). The replacement energy is passed to the pendulum by means of an escapement mechanism which gives a slight push to the top of the pendulum once in each swing. It is most important that the slight push should come at the right moment in the pendulum's swing: if it comes at the wrong moment it may bring the movement to a halt instead of maintaining it. (This is easily demonstrated with a child's swing. If it is given a push just after it changes direction its to-and-fro motion is maintained or even increased. But if it is given a push just before it changes direction it quickly stops swinging altogether.) Electrical oscillations, too, can be maintained by feeding energy into the circuit at the right moment in each oscillation. For this purpose the triode valve — which has been encountered already in the role of amplifier — is ideally suited.

The tuned circuit (coil and capacitor) is connected to the grid of the triode. When the power supply is switched on there is normally a surge of electrons to the grid. This initial surge sets up oscillations in the grid circuit. The output from the anode oscillates with exactly the same frequency but because the triode acts as an amplifier the amplitude (peak values) of these oscillations is greater than the amplitude of the input oscillations on the grid. The extra energy has been drawn from the high tension supply. By *feeding back* some of the energy from the anode circuit to the grid circuit the energy lost as heat is replaced and the oscillations can be prevented from dying away. This is the principle of all valve oscillators. Because the anode oscillations have the same frequency as the grid oscillations

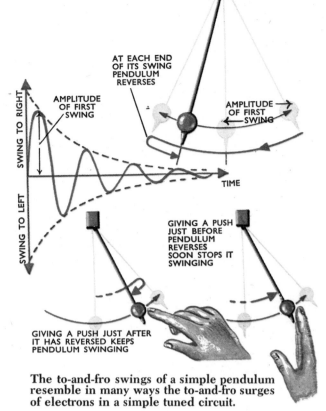

The to-and-fro swings of a simple pendulum resemble in many ways the to-and-fro surges of electrons in a simple tuned circuit.

the energy pulses fed back to the grid can easily be arranged to arrive at the right moment, like the energy fed from the clock spring to the pendulum.

How the energy is fed back is seen most easily in the simple tuned grid oscillator (or Armstrong oscillator as it is sometimes called). This has a coil in its anode circuit mounted very close to the coil in the tuned circuit attached to the grid. Together the two coils act as a transformer. Amplified oscillations in the anode coil produce a changing magnetic field which cuts through the nearby coil in the tuned circuit. The changing magnetic field sets up voltage oscillations in the tuned circuit coil having the same frequency as the original oscillations. In this way energy is fed from the anode circuit to the grid circuit even though there is no electrical link between the two.

As might be expected such a simple arrangement as the Armstrong oscillator suffers from a number of shortcomings. It does not work well at very high frequencies, and most serious of all, the frequency of the oscillations tends to change of its own accord. This latter defect is known as frequency *instability*.

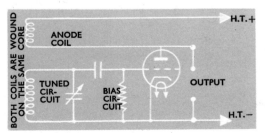

BASIC (ARMSTRONG) OSCILLATOR

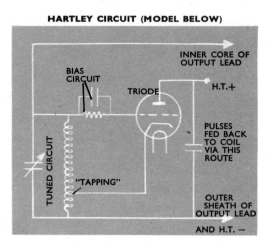

HARTLEY CIRCUIT (MODEL BELOW)

INNER CORE OF OUTPUT LEAD

BIAS CIRCUIT

TRIODE

H.T.+

PULSES FED BACK TO COIL VIA THIS ROUTE

TUNED CIRCUIT

"TAPPING"

OUTER SHEATH OF OUTPUT LEAD

AND H.T. —

is 'tapped' can usually be altered to adjust the amount of energy fed back to the grid circuit. If too little energy is fed back the oscillations will not be maintained. It is, however, equally necessary to ensure that not too much energy is fed back, otherwise the oscillations build up until the grid of the triode becomes positively charged for some part of each oscillation. Should this happen the valve ceases to conduct, so energy is fed back and the whole process begins again. The effect of this is to add a second, uncontrollable variation to the oscillation — in other words it results in instability.

The Colpitts oscillator

The Colpitts oscillator works on a similar principle to that of the Hartley oscillator except that the single coil is not tapped. Instead two capacitors are connected across it, and current oscillations are fed back at the junction between these two capacitors instead of at some point on the coil. Such an arrangement is easier to tune (i.e. to alter the frequency of the oscillations produced) than the basic Armstrong circuit. The Colpitts and the Hartley oscillators are equally good electronically. Additional components can be inserted into either circuit to improve the stability. Both

The Hartley oscillator

The Hartley oscillator is an improvement on the basic Armstrong circuit. Instead of having a separate coil in the anode circuit, part of the tuned circuit is 'tapped off' and some of the output oscillations from the anode are passed through this section. Current oscillations in the tapped off section set up voltage oscillations across the whole of the coil, thus supplying the energy needed to compensate for losses in the tuned circuit. The point at which the coil

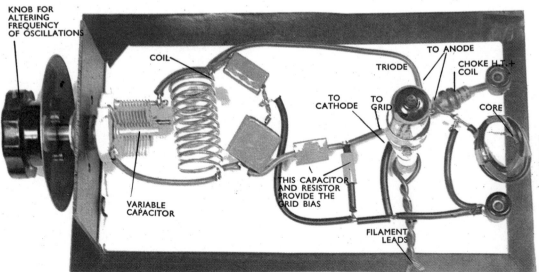

KNOB FOR ALTERING FREQUENCY OF OSCILLATIONS

COIL

TO ANODE

TRIODE

CHOKE H.T.+ COIL

TO CATHODE

TO GRID

CORE

THIS CAPACITOR AND RESISTOR PROVIDE THE GRID BIAS

VARIABLE CAPACITOR

OUTPUT LEADS

FILAMENT LEADS

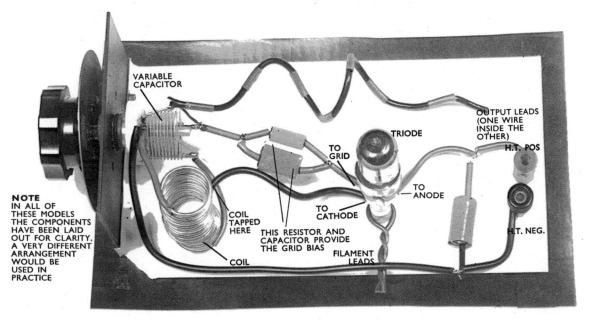

VARIABLE
CAPACITOR

TRIODE

OUTPUT LEADS
(ONE WIRE
INSIDE THE
OTHER)

H.T. POS

TO
GRID

TO
ANODE

TO
CATHODE

H.T. NEG.

NOTE
IN ALL OF
THESE MODELS
THE COMPONENTS
HAVE BEEN LAID
OUT FOR CLARITY.
A VERY DIFFERENT
ARRANGEMENT
WOULD BE
USED IN
PRACTICE

COIL
TAPPED
HERE

THIS RESISTOR AND
CAPACITOR PROVIDE
THE GRID BIAS

FILAMENT
LEADS

COIL

types provide very convenient devices for producing oscillations of any frequency and any size up to the limits at which the triode valve will work.

THE FIXED FREQUENCY OSCILLATOR

The tuning knob on a radio receiver is connected to a variable capacitor. Turning the knob alters the value of this capacitor and hence the *frequency* to which the tuned circuit (simply the variable capacitor and a coil of wire) responds. Now the frequency of any particular radio wave is the same as the frequency of the to-and-fro surges of electrons set up by the *oscillator* in the transmitter. A few simple oscillators have already been described and it was seen that the frequency of the electron surges was controlled by a tuned circuit basically similar to that which tunes a radio receiver. If these simple oscillators were in fact used in radio transmitters the result would be very unhappy. To listen to a radio programme would involve moving the tuning knob of the receiver all the time to try and catch up with the programme as it drifted up and down the tuning dial. Worse still, one broadcast would get mixed up with another, and clear, steady television

pictures would be almost unknown. The reason for this gloomy state of affairs? Simply that the radio *carrier wave* (on which the sound signal is superimposed) from each transmitter must have its own unvarying frequency, and the oscillators described hitherto are incapable of producing electron surges of very constant frequencies. The oscillators used in actual transmitters are *fixed frequency* oscillators — they produce electron surges whose frequencies are practically constant. Frequency stability is obtained here with the aid of *electron-coupling* and *crystal control*. Before examining these two improvements it is helpful to review the defects of the simple oscillatory circuit.

First of all it has been assumed up to now that a tuned circuit either accepts or rejects electron surges of just one

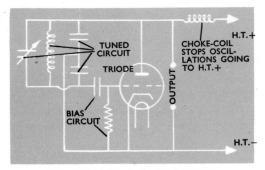

TUNED
CIRCUIT

TRIODE

CHOKE-COIL
STOPS OSCIL-
LATIONS GOING
TO H.T.+

H.T.+

OUTPUT

BIAS
CIRCUIT

H.T.—

COLPITTS CIRCUIT (MODEL ABOVE)

particular frequency. In fact this is not the case. A theoretical capacitor-and-coil circuit does show a maximum response to its tuned or resonant frequency but it also responds appreciably to frequencies just above and just below the resonant frequency. An actual capacitor-and-coil circuit is bound to have some resistance which has the effect of widening the range of frequencies to which the circuit responds. A carelessly constructed circuit will respond indiscriminately to quite a wide band of frequencies.

Secondly, we have so far neglected the effect which the circuit connected to the output of the oscillator has on the frequency of the oscillations. In fact the 'load' connected to the output forms part of the anode circuit, and since the anode circuit is linked to the grid circuit (as it must be in order to feed back enough energy to stop the oscillations in the grid circuit from dying away) it is only to be expected that any change in the 'load' will have a profound effect upon the tuned (grid) circuit. In other words the frequency of a simple oscillator is steady if only every bit of every circuit which comes after the oscillator remains fixed.

Crystal controlled oscillators overcome the first defect (the wide frequency response of a capacitor-and-coil circuit). The principle of crystal control is simply that a slice of quartz will vibrate mechanically (like a tuning fork) with a definite fundamental fre-

A theoretical circuit of a Tuned-Anode Tuned-Grid (T.A.T.G.) oscillator.

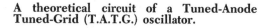

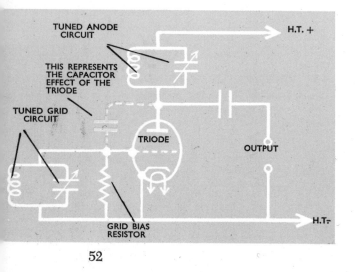

quency. It will also vibrate with twice or three times the fundamental frequency but these 'harmonic' vibrations are so far removed from the fundamental that they are unlikely to cause trouble. The fundamental frequency depends upon the dimensions of the slice of quartz, and once the crystal has been cut and mounted its frequency of vibration is remarkably constant. Quartz is one of the few substances which shows the *piezo-electric* effect: – if a slice of quartz is stretched or compressed a voltage develops between opposite faces. If a slice is made to *vibrate* an *alternating* voltage develops. The reverse is also true: – if an alternating voltage is connected across two metal plates on opposite faces of a slice of quartz it is set vibrating with its own definite frequency. Thus a quartz crystal can be used in place of the capacitor-and-coil circuit in an oscillator. The vibrating crystal produces a small voltage oscillation in the grid circuit of a valve and an alternating voltage fed back to the crystal from the anode circuit keeps it vibrating. If it is necessary to change the frequency of the oscillations the crystal has to be unplugged from the circuit and replaced by another crystal having the required fundamental frequency.

The circuit generally used when crystal control is employed is known as the *tuned-anode tuned-grid circuit* (TATG for short). A TATG circuit diagram is illustrated on the left and it will be seen from this diagram that no *direct* link exists between the grid circuit and the anode circuit. The energy needed to compensate for heat losses in the grid circuit and hence to keep the oscillations going is fed back from the anode circuit *via the valve itself.* This is possible with a triode valve because the grid (negatively charged) is close to the anode (positively charged) and these two oppositely charged electrodes act just like the plates of a capacitor. High frequency oscillations pass with ease through a capacitor and therefore they can leak back from anode to grid. In fact it is to *prevent* such a leak of energy that a pentode (five-electrode) valve is normally used in high frequency amplifiers. If the tuned-grid circuit of a TATG oscillator is replaced

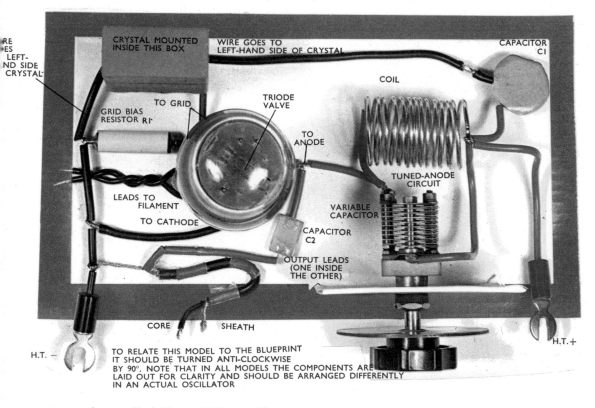

RE
ES
LEFT-
ND SIDE
CRYSTAL

CRYSTAL MOUNTED INSIDE THIS BOX

WIRE GOES TO LEFT-HAND SIDE OF CRYSTAL

CAPACITOR CI

TO GRID

GRID BIAS RESISTOR RI

TRIODE VALVE

COIL

TO ANODE

TUNED-ANODE CIRCUIT

LEADS TO FILAMENT

TO CATHODE

VARIABLE CAPACITOR

CAPACITOR C2

OUTPUT LEADS (ONE INSIDE THE OTHER)

CORE   SHEATH

H.T. —

H.T.+

TO RELATE THIS MODEL TO THE BLUEPRINT IT SHOULD BE TURNED ANTI-CLOCKWISE BY 90°. NOTE THAT IN ALL MODELS THE COMPONENTS ARE LAID OUT FOR CLARITY AND SHOULD BE ARRANGED DIFFERENTLY IN AN ACTUAL OSCILLATOR

A crystal-controlled Pierce-Miller oscillator. The corresponding circuit diagram is shown below. To relate the model to the diagram, the model should be turned anti-clockwise by 90° (so that the black H.T.—.wire is at the bottom). Note that in all models the components are laid out for clarity, and would be arranged differently in an actual oscillator.

by a quartz crystal the result is the Pierce-Miller circuit illustrated above.

Crystal controlled oscillators, as well as eliminating the frequency defects of a capacitor-and-coil circuit, are not seriously affected by the second shortcoming of simple oscillators—the frequency variation caused by changes in the load. *Electron-coupled* oscillators overcome this second defect in a different manner. Electron-coupling can be applied to virtually any oscillator circuit. It consists of putting a pentode valve in place of the triode. The pentode has a cathode, control grid and anode like those of a triode, but it has in addition a screen grid and a suppressor grid between the control grid and the anode. In an electron coupled oscillator (ECO for short) the pentode is used in such a way that the cathode, control grid and screen grid corres-

pond to the cathode, control grid and anode of a triode valve. This 'internal triode' is wired up as a normal triode oscillator and in consequence the flow of electrons to the anode is made to vary in an oscillatory manner. Because there is no direct linkage between the grid circuit and the anode circuit any alteration

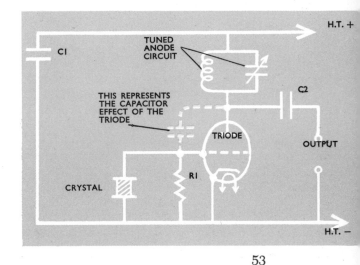

CI

TUNED ANODE CIRCUIT

THIS REPRESENTS THE CAPACITOR EFFECT OF THE TRIODE

H.T. +

C2

TRIODE

OUTPUT

CRYSTAL

RI

H.T. —

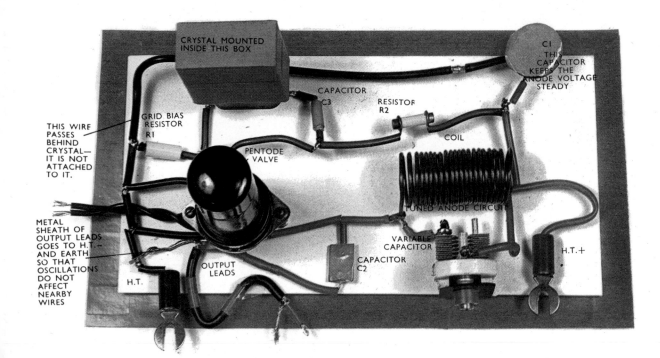

CRYSTAL MOUNTED INSIDE THIS BOX

C1 THIS CAPACITOR KEEPS THE ANODE VOLTAGE STEADY

CAPACITOR C3

RESISTOR R2

THIS WIRE PASSES BEHIND CRYSTAL— IT IS NOT ATTACHED TO IT.

GRID BIAS RESISTOR R1

COIL

PENTODE VALVE

TUNED ANODE CIRCUIT

METAL SHEATH OF OUTPUT LEADS GOES TO H.T.— AND EARTH SO THAT OSCILLATIONS DO NOT AFFECT NEARBY WIRES

VARIABLE CAPACITOR

H.T.+

H.T.

OUTPUT LEADS

CAPACITOR C2

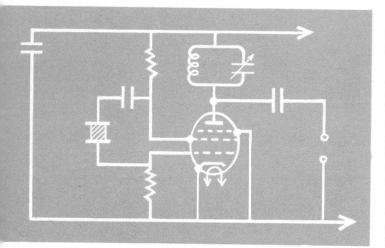

A crystal controlled Pierce-Colpitts oscillator employing a pentode valve and electron-coupling.

made to the output circuit is not reflected in the grid circuit.

The Pierce-Colpitts circuit illustrated here employs a pentode with electron-coupling as well as crystal control. This makes doubly sure that the frequency of the resulting oscillations is stable and does not drift above or below its fixed value. The only factor which could cause the frequency to vary is a change of temperature. Like everything else quartz expands on heating and a change in size of a quartz crystal will alter its fundamental frequency of vibration. To prevent this happening in a powerful transmitter the crystal is placed in a constant temperature enclosure controlled by a thermostat.

Radio Transmission

THE APPARATUS used to broadcast radio signals is called a *radio transmitter* and, as usual, it can be considered as a series of *stages* or blocks of electronic equipment.

The first stage of a transmitter is a microphone which changes the sound into a series of pulses of electricity, known as the *audio frequency signal* (since they are of an audible frequency). These pulses are extremely small so, in order to make them big enough to have an appreciable effect on the rest of the apparatus, they are passed to an *audio frequency amplifier*.

If, now that the signal has been made amplified, it could be broadcast, it would become hopelessly mixed up with all the radio signals being broadcast from other transmitters. This would mean that a radio receiver would pick up these signals all at the same time and a babble would come from the loudspeaker. It has already been explained under the

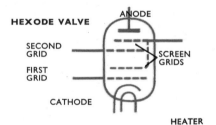

HEXODE VALVE

ANODE
SECOND GRID
FIRST GRID
SCREEN GRIDS
CATHODE
HEATER

diode detector (see page 30) that this difficulty is overcome by combining a constant high frequency series of pulses (called the carrier wave) with the audio frequency. This signal—which may be produced by one of the fixed frequency oscillators previously described—has the effect of giving the two signals the single frequency of the carrier. However, the *amplitude* (i.e. the strength) of the new signal now varies with the frequency of the audio signal.

The two signals are combined using a stage called a *modulator*. This is quite straightforward and could use a valve like the triode but now with two grids instead of just one. If one signal is applied to each grid then the stream of electrons passing through the valve is affected by both signals together so that the current appearing at the anode has the two frequencies mixed. In practice it is found that with the simple valve described the grids affect each other as well as the electron stream and this causes the effect of each to be complicated. This is not at all what is wanted. Hence two more grids connected to earth (through a suitable bias resistor) are put into the valve to separate the two signal grids, stopping their effect from reaching one another's circuits. Hence the valve

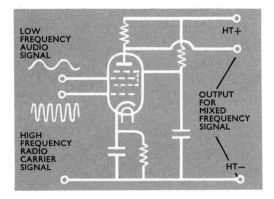

LOW FREQUENCY AUDIO SIGNAL

HT+

OUTPUT FOR MIXED FREQUENCY SIGNAL

HIGH FREQUENCY RADIO CARRIER SIGNAL

HT−

The audio frequency (sound) signal modulates the radio frequency (carrier) signal using a six-electrode (hexode) valve.

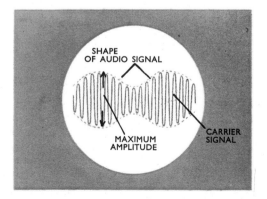

SHAPE OF AUDIO SIGNAL

MAXIMUM AMPLITUDE

CARRIER SIGNAL

Oscilloscope displaying the output from the modulator. Frequency is that of the carrier signal but the *amplitude* varies in time with the audio signal.

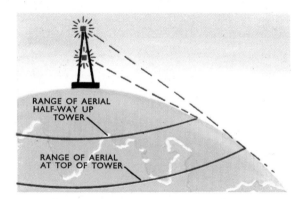

The height of a transmitting aerial governs the range at which its signals can be received on the ground. The taller the mast the greater is the area served.

now has six electrodes altogether and so is called a *hexode valve.*

If the radio signal has to travel more than a few miles then it must be made very strong. Hence it is next passed through a *radio frequency amplifier.* However, in a powerful transmitter the pulses must be very big and a small valve with fine grids held in glass will soon become very hot and melt. Much larger valves, sometimes several feet long, must then be used, and they must be cooled continuously by blowing a stream of air over them. However the way in which this *high-power radio frequency amplifier* works is just the same as in the smaller case.

The very strong pulses of the radio signal are now passed to the *aerial* which is a metal plate or wire in which the electrons move in time with the radio signal. This causes electromagnetic radio waves to be formed and these radiate in

all directions from the aerial. Transmitting aerials on masts on high ground round the countryside are a common sight. It must not be thought that the whole mast is the aerial. In fact the aerial part is put right at the top of the mast since the radio waves can then travel a longer distance, as can be seen from the diagram.

Hence the radio signal is now sent out in all directions to be picked up by the smaller aerial of a radio receiver and converted back into the original sound which entered the microphone.

RADIO WAVES

Radio waves are sent out when bursts of electric current pass along a transmitting aerial. The waves are in the form of *electromagnetic* radiation because they are created as a result of the magnetic and electric fields set up when the current flows in the aerial.

The aerial forms part of the output circuit of the transmitter, and in this circuit electrical oscillations are generated. This means that electric currents pass to and fro in the circuit a constant number of times each second. The number of oscillations each second is called the *frequency*, and each complete to and fro motion is called a *cycle*. So, if the current passes to and fro 50 times a second the frequency of the oscillation is 50 cycles per second (50 c/s).

The electrical oscillations fed to the aerial cause the electric and magnetic fields around the aerial to swell up and die away with the same frequency as the oscillations. The radiation from the

Mixing two 'signals': the to-and-fro pendulum movement (representing the carrier signal) is being *modulated* by the up-and-down finger movement (representing the audio signal). The resulting trace illustrates an amplitude-modulated wave.

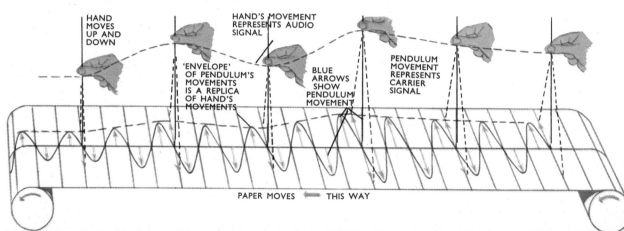

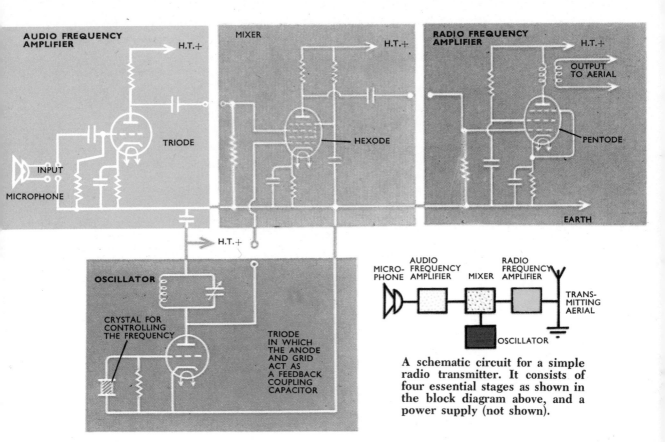

A schematic circuit for a simple radio transmitter. It consists of four essential stages as shown in the block diagram above, and a power supply (not shown).

aerial consists of a series of peaks and troughs of electromagnetic energy emitted at that frequency.

All electromagnetic waves travel at the speed of light (which is itself a form of electromagnetic wave motion) i.e. 3×10^{10} centimetres per second. An aerial transmitting radio waves of frequency, say, 10,000 c/s is producing 10,000 (10^4) waves every second. These would occupy 3×10^{10} centimetres if placed end to end, so the length of each wave *(the wavelength)* is

$$\frac{3 \times 10^{10}}{10^4} = 3 \times 10^6 \text{ centimetres or 30,000}$$

metres.

All electromagnetic waves (radio or light waves) can be described either by their wavelengths or by their frequencies. The wavelength can automatically be found from the frequency, and vice versa. Radio waves are often specified by their wavelengths.

When a radio wave of a certain wavelength is transmitted from an aerial it can be picked up by the receiving aerial where it is reconverted into electrical currents which alternate at the transmission frequency.

If the aerial is receiving several waves of different wavelength simultaneously the receiving circuit can be 'tuned' to select just one wavelength for amplification. This is what happens in an ordinary radio set. The aerial is receiving many hundreds of radio signals transmitted from stations all over the world, but only one is selected at the receiver, by 'tuning in' on a single wavelength.

If, however, the signal received were a single 'pure' wavelength of radio frequency, the received signal would be completely inaudible. The frequencies are far too high for the human ear to detect. In addition, to transmit information (e.g. speech or music) the wave has to be *modulated*.

A radio wave must be able to carry information which is a mixture of signals of all audible frequencies. In an *amplitude modulated* wave a signal is transmitted at a given frequency (the carrier frequency), but the waves are altered in *amplitude* (size) by the information the wave has to carry. For example, a broadcasting station may make its transmission at 200,000 c/s.

57

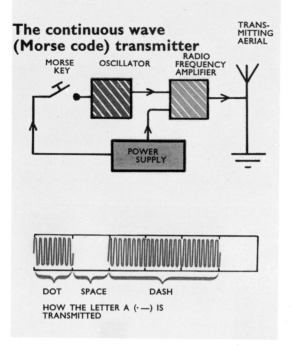

The continuous wave (Morse code) transmitter

MORSE KEY — OSCILLATOR — RADIO FREQUENCY AMPLIFIER

TRANS-MITTING AERIAL

POWER SUPPLY

DOT SPACE DASH

HOW THE LETTER A (· —) IS TRANSMITTED

Since Morse code consists of dots and dashes a message can be transmitted in code by simply chopping up the carrier wave into long bursts and short bursts. The continuous wave (C-W) transmitter does not need an audio frequency amplifier or a mixer stage. The Morse key is arranged so that it interrupts the power supplied to the oscillator or to the radio frequency amplifier. When the key is pressed the circuit is completed and a continuous train of waves is broadcast. If the key is held down a long train of waves (a 'dash') results, but if it is held down only briefly a short burst of waves (a 'dot') is broadcast instead. While the key is open no waves are broadcast at all. The circuit containing the key is provided with coils and capacitors to eliminate the 'clicks' which occur at the moment when the key is opened or closed.

The radio waves are transmitted at this frequency but the sizes of the waves are being continuously altered to carry the information being broadcast.

The receiver is tuned to 200,000 c/s (1,500 metres) so it is able to receive and amplify the signal. When the signal passes through a *detector* stage the information contained in the wave modulation is extracted for further amplification.

Suppose the 200,000 c/s is being modulated at a frequency of 1,000 cycles per second. Although the transmitted wave is a pure 200,000 c/s wave, it acts as if it is a mixture of *three* waves of frequency 200,000 c/s, 200,000 − 1,000 = 199,000 c/s, and 200,000 + 1,000 = 201,000 c/s. This can be proved mathematically. A modulated wave has then a main *carrier* of frequency 200,000 c/s and two *sidebands* of frequency 201,000 c/s and 199,000 c/s. It therefore 'occupies' a frequency *band* 2,000 cycles 'wide', from 199,000 c/s to 201,000 c/s. This is of great importance when it comes to allocating wavelengths to different broadcasting stations. If one station wishes to broadcast speech at a carrier frequency of 200,000 cycles per second, then another station broadcasting at 198,000 cycles per second will overlap the first station's 'band' because the frequencies of the side bands due to transmission of speech or music will be well into the first station's bandwidth. For this reason,

each station, by international agreement, keeps not only to its own carrier frequency, but also to a limited *bandwidth*.

The large number of radio stations thus occupy the 'air', each restricting its transmission to within a narrow range of frequencies.

Broadcast transmissions are normally transmitted in one of three *wavebands* each of which covers a range of wavelengths. A large number of stations transmit at wavelengths within each waveband. Transmissions over small and intermediate distances are normally made on the *long* and *medium* wavebands. Long waveband broadcasts are usually made at radio wavelengths greater than 1,000 metres, and medium ones in the wavelength range 100 to 1,000 metres. Transmissions over larger distances are made on the *short* waveband, of wavelength 50 metres or less.

These divisions are made because of the behaviour of the waves transmitted from an aerial at different wavelengths. The radio waves normally spread out in all directions. Those which pass along the ground are called *ground waves*. The *space waves* hit the ground at a point somewhere between the aerial and the horizon. *Sky waves* are directed towards the sky, to miss the horizon.

It so happens that most of the energy in a longer wavelength transmission is radiated in the ground wave, which can

WAVELENGTH

Wavelength	Band	Application
100,000 metres (62½ miles)		
10,000 ,,		
1,000 ,,	Long Wave Band	RADIO
100 ,,	Medium Wave Band	Broadcasting Bands
10 ,,	Short Wave Band	
1 ,,	Ultra Short Wave Band	Radio Telephone and *Two-way Communication*
10 centimetres 1 centimetre 1 millimetre (1,000 microns)	Microwave Band	RADAR
100 microns 10 ,, 1 micron (1 millionth of a metre)	Infra-Red	
	Visible Light	
1,000 Ångstrom units 100 ,, ,, (1 millionth of a centimetre) 10 ,, ,, 1 ,, ,, 1/10 ,, ,,	X-Rays	
1/100 ,, ,, 1/1000 ,, ,,	Gamma Rays	

The range of frequencies used for commercial broadcasting purposes is very great. For sound broadcasting the carriers must be separated by at least 15,000 c/s and so this would also have to be the lowest carrier frequency. For television transmission the modulating frequency range is about 10,000,000 c/s wide and the carrier frequency has therefore to be much higher.

The highest frequencies used commercially extend to about 2,000,000,000 c/s or 2,000 Mega-cycles/sec. Two-way communication and radar applications extend the range to just below the infra-red or lowest part of the visible light range or spectrum (1 millimetre wavelength).

extend to a distance of 1,000 miles. Long wavelength transmissions are mainly used for short distances. The same applies, to a lesser extent, to the medium waves which are also used for transmissions over distances of up to 200 miles from the transmitter.

At shorter wavelengths a strong sky-wave transmission is obtained. At these wavelengths charged layers of the earth's atmosphere possess the property of reflecting back the radio-waves. These layers are used for sending short wave transmissions over great distances, by reflecting the skywaves back to earth at great distances from the transmitter.

The wavelength, frequency, and velocity of a wave are related by $\text{wavelength} = \dfrac{\text{velocity}}{\text{frequency}}$

WAVELENGTH

DIRECTION OF TRAVEL OF TRANSMITTED WAVE

Television

ALTHOUGH television is now taken for granted in many homes, the development of a cheap and reliable method of transmitting and receiving pictures and sound is a remarkable achievement.

In sound broadcasting, a microphone picks up the sounds and converts them into electrical signals that are amplified and turned into a form of electromagnetic waves. These are capable of being transmitted over long distances. In television, an electronic camera picks up a picture and translates the optical image into a series of electrical impulses. These, too, are amplified and processed so that *video* (visual) information may be sent, using electromagnetic waves, over long distances. The video signals have to be accompanied by sound signals so that, say, the lip movements on the screen tie in with the words spoken. Then, when the waves strike the receiver aerial, the receiver is able to make a faithful reproduction in sound and vision of the scene in the studio.

The Television Camera

Cine cameras photograph moving objects by taking many still photographs in one second. When these are projected and presented to the human eye the effect of smooth continuous motion is produced. In a television set, using the same principle, 50 complete pictures are presented every second. This, however, is practically the only similarity between the two. The two systems differ because a complete frame cannot be transmitted at a particular instant in time by a television transmitter but only the detail in one small part of the scene is transmitted at one instant. The scene presented to a television camera is *scanned*.

The difference between the two methods can be seen more clearly by considering two ways of looking at a book. The eyes can take in an illustration almost at a glance. This corresponds to the way a cine camera takes one

frame. To digest the information contained in newsprint, however, the eyes rest on one word at a time and progress from left to right across a line. At the end of a line they move back to the left hand side of the next line and so on until they finish the page. This corresponds to the way the television camera scans a scene.

In the television camera, an image of the scene is projected by a system of lenses on to a small mosaic screen. The screen is covered with minute cells, each one quite separate and insulated from the others. Each cell can liberate a number of electrons when light falls on it. As long as light falls on a cell, it gains electric charge. The stronger the light, the greater the charge that accumulates. To transmit the image falling on the mosaic screen the tiny cells must be scanned in turn to see how much charge each cell has gained.

The scanning is done by a beam of electrons which are generated at the cathode of the camera tube and accelerated towards and past the anode. The

The scene focused on the screen causes the tiny mosaic elements to become electrically charged. The scanning electron beam neutralises the charge on each element in turn, causing current to flow in the resistor R. The train of pulses passing through R is passed on to an amplifier.

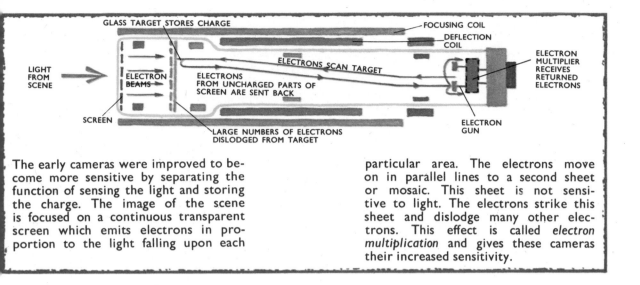

GLASS TARGET STORES CHARGE — FOCUSING COIL

DEFLECTION COIL

LIGHT FROM SCENE

ELECTRON BEAMS

ELECTRONS SCAN TARGET

ELECTRONS FROM UNCHARGED PARTS OF SCREEN ARE SENT BACK

ELECTRON MULTIPLIER RECEIVES RETURNED ELECTRONS

SCREEN

LARGE NUMBERS OF ELECTRONS DISLODGED FROM TARGET

ELECTRON GUN

The early cameras were improved to become more sensitive by separating the function of sensing the light and storing the charge. The image of the scene is focused on a continuous transparent screen which emits electrons in proportion to the light falling upon each particular area. The electrons move on in parallel lines to a second sheet or mosaic. This sheet is not sensitive to light. The electrons strike this sheet and dislodge many other electrons. This effect is called *electron multiplication* and gives these cameras their increased sensitivity.

grid controls the strength of the beam. This whole assembly is called the 'gun'. Pairs of horizontal and vertical deflection coils deflect the beam to scan the cells. As the beam passes over the tiny cells it discharges each cell in turn and creates a succession of current surges that are fed to a resistor. The varying voltage produced across the resistor by the current pulses is then amplified. These varying voltage pulses represent the brightness of fragments of the scene being televised. When these voltage variations are transmitted to a television receiver they are used to vary the brightness of the screen of the television

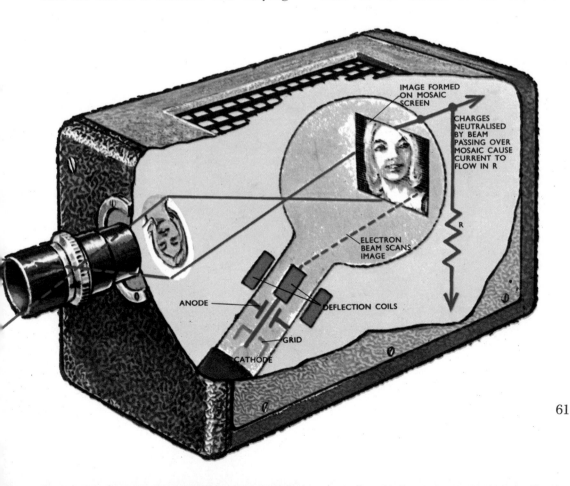

IMAGE FORMED ON MOSAIC SCREEN

CHARGES NEUTRALISED BY BEAM PASSING OVER MOSAIC CAUSE CURRENT TO FLOW IN R

R

ELECTRON BEAM SCANS IMAGE

ANODE

DEFLECTION COILS

GRID

CATHODE

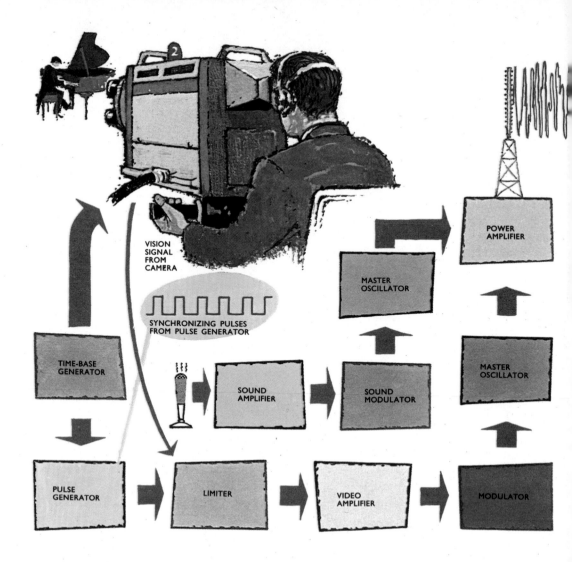

VISION
SIGNAL
FROM
CAMERA

SYNCHRONIZING PULSES
FROM PULSE GENERATOR

TIME-BASE
GENERATOR

MASTER
OSCILLATOR

POWER
AMPLIFIER

SOUND
AMPLIFIER

SOUND
MODULATOR

MASTER
OSCILLATOR

PULSE
GENERATOR

LIMITER

VIDEO
AMPLIFIER

MODULATOR

At the transmitter. Video pulses from the camera are mixed with synchronizing pulses from time-bas generator. These are impressed on the very high frequency oscillating signals from the master oscillator, by the modulator. The final modulated signal is amplified and transmitted. The sound signal is transmitted at a slightly higher frequency than the visic signal. The high frequency wave train is generated at a separate master oscillator.

receiver at exactly the same points in the scanning cycle. The original scene is thus re-created on the cathode ray tube screen.

Scanning the Picture

The beam of electrons in the camera has to be deflected to sweep along the light sensitive screen. Specially shaped pulses from the *time base generator* are passed through the deflection coils.

These make the electron beam scan the screen, line by line, so that the beam starts off at the top left hand corner, and finishes at the bottom right hand corner.

The Transmitted Signal

By scanning the picture, a series of electrical pulses representing the brightness of small elements in the scene is produced. Microphones in the studio produce a succession of pulses that

62

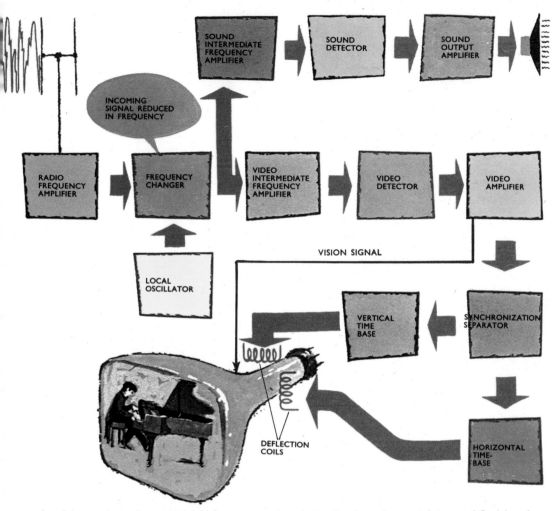

At the receiver the very high frequency signal received at the aerial is amplified by the radio frequency amplifier. It is reduced in frequency by pumping in a wave train from the local oscillator. The sound and vision signals are then separated and amplified before being detected. The detected sound signal is used to drive the loudspeaker. The detected vision signal is used to vary the voltage on the grid of the cathode ray tube, and the synchronization pulse is used to make the time base circuits operate in step with time base generator in the camera.

represent the sound. A further set of signals is also necessary to produce effective television. These are needed to *synchronize* the television receiver with the television camera. This means that if, say, the electron beam in the camera is 'reading' the right corner of the camera screen, then the electron beam in the television tube is 'writing' on the top right corner of the television tube.

The electrical pulses that drive the electron beam back and forth across the face of the camera are also used to provide the *synchronizing pulses*.

So the vision signal and synchronizing pulses are transmitted together. They are impressed together on to an electrical wave that oscillates back and forth at tens or hundreds of millions of times each second. The sound signal is also transmitted at a similar frequency.

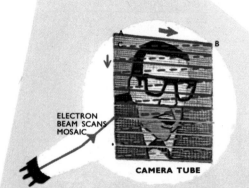

CAMERA TUBE

In the *sequential* scanning system the electron beam scans one line of the mosaic, from left to right (A to B) very quickly 'flies back' to the beginning of the next line. The beam of electron in the cathode ray tube of the receiver copies the movement of the camera beam, drawing a replica of the original scene.

CATHODE RAY TUBE

By making the *size* of the oscillating wave vary with time, the information that the signals represent is carried from the transmitter to the receiver.

The time base synchronizing signals are turned into a suitable form in a *pulse generator* and fed, together with the video signal, to a video *amplifier*. They then pass to a *modulator* where they, together with the sound signals, are impressed on to high frequency oscillations produced by the *master oscillator*. This produces the modulated wave carrying all the required information. After amplification, it passes to the transmitter.

The Television Receiver

The electromagnetic waves sent out by the transmitter aerial strike the receiver aerial and induce electrical signals in it.

The receiver first of all amplifies these signals because although they were very powerful when they left the transmitter they will probably be very weak when they reach the receiver. Then, the very high frequency oscillations, modulated with sound, vision and synchronization signals have to be separated.

Each broadcasting station transmits in its own frequency 'channel'. The range of frequency channels extends from

The electron beam sweeps out a mosaic on the face of the cathode ray tube. The signals fed to the grid of the tube affect the number of electrons hitting the phosphor so that the brightness of the spot on the face varies. The variations in brightness enable the picture to be 'drawn' by the beam.

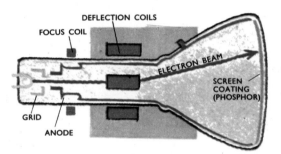

about 40 million cycles per second (40 Mc/s), to about 900 Mc/s. The required channel is selected at the receiver.

Signals of frequency 40—215 Mc/s are called Very High Frequency signals (V.H.F.). As the lower radio frequencies become filled, and interference between transmitting stations becomes inevitable at these lower frequencies, some radio programmes are now being transmitted, not as amplitude-modulated waves, but as frequency-modulated waves.

The higher frequencies used for television transmissions are called Ultra High Frequencies (U.H.F.). The highest frequencies used, about 900 Mc/s, correspond to a radio wave only about a foot long.

The frequency of the signal is much too high to be amplified properly, so its frequency is reduced by mixing it with an oscillating signal that is always a set frequency higher than the incoming signal. The effect is to produce a 'difference' signal, the *intermediate frequency signal.*

This mixing process is carried out in the *frequency changer.*

The signal emerging from the frequency changer is modulated with the vision signal and with the sound signal. The signal is then *detected*, and the sound and vision signals extracted. The sound signal passes after amplification to the loudspeaker. The vision signal, after amplification, passes to the cathode ray tube. The synchronizing pulses are carried along with the video signal and are fed to the time-base units. These units produce currents that make the electron beam sweep out the raster on the cathode ray tube face in step with the 'scan' at the camera. The synchronizing pulses make sure that the scan of the cathode ray tube keeps time with the scan in the camera.

Producing the Picture

In the receiver, a beam of electrons sweeps back and forth across the face of the cathode ray tube. The face is coated with a *phosphor* that glows when it is struck by the electrons.

The brightness of the glow is controlled by varying the voltage on the

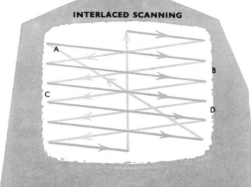

INTERLACED SCANNING

Each complete scanned picture is called a *frame*. If only a few frames were shown in one second the result would be that the screen would appear to flicker. If more than about 50 frames per second are shown the flicker disappears and a steady picture results. It is found that if certain difficulties are to be avoided the number of pictures per second must be related to the mains frequency. Thus for 50 c/s mains supplies the frame frequency must be 25 or 50 cycles per second. It is found that 25 frames per second is not quite high enough to eliminate flicker, so that 50 frames per second is used. An ingeneous method is used to reduce the amount of information which would have to be transmitted if 50 *complete* frames were transmitted each second. The method is called 'interlaced scanning'. The travelling. spot on the cathode ring tube traces out parallel lines on the screen, but there is a gap between adjacent lines which is twice the gap used in sequential scanning. The spot traces out alternate lines.

grid of the tube. This controls the number of electrons reaching the phosphor. The electron beam is moved in the tube by passing, as in the camera, currents through deflection coils. There is a vertical coil and a horizontal coil. The currents to the coils are produced by the *time base circuits,* and these circuits are 'locked' to the synchronizing pulses received from the transmitter.

So, as the beam moves down the tube, line by line, the brightness signal fed to the grid makes it draw lines of varying brightness—corresponding to the brightness of the lines in the original scanned picture in the camera.

COMPONENTS IN THE SIMPLE RADIO RECEIVER (PAGES 36-39)

The circuit diagram shown on pages 38 and 39 has been designed to illustrate the principles involved in the operation of the various stages of a simple receiver. It is not intended to be used in the construction of a working model, and the component values listed below are given only as examples of typical components that might be used:

C_1 is part of a gauged variable capacitor typical value $0.0005\mu F$.

R_1	$= 50K\Omega$	C_6	$= 25\mu F$
R_4	$= 200K\Omega$	R_6	$= 2000\Omega$
C_2	$= 0.01\mu F$	C_7	$= 0.01\mu F$
C_3	$= 25\mu F$	R_7	$= 1M\Omega$
R_2	$= 330\Omega$	R_8	$= 100K\Omega$
R_3	$= 2000\Omega$	C_8	$= 25\mu F$
C_4	$= 0.01\mu F$	R_9	$= 470\Omega$
R_5	$= 10K\Omega$	C_9	$= 0.1\mu F$
C_5	as C_1		

$1F = 1$ Farad

$1\mu F = 1$ microfarad $= \dfrac{1}{1,000,000}$ Farad

$1\Omega = 1$ ohm

$1K\Omega = 1$ Kilo/ohm $= 1,000$ ohms

$1M\Omega = 1$ Megaohm $= 1,000,000$ ohms

PART TWO

Semiconductors and Transistors

Semi-conductor Diodes

WHEN THE ends of an electrical *conductor*, such as a piece of copper wire, are connected to the terminals of a battery an electric current flows through the conductor. This means that there is a large continuous transfer of negative charge (electrons) from the negative plate *(cathode)* of the battery through the wire to the positive plate *(anode)*. This transfer of charge occurs because a number of free electrons are free to move within the wire.

However, when an electrical *insulator*, such as mica, is connected between the battery terminals there is almost no transfer of charge. This is because the atoms of the insulator do not have any free or easily removed electrons and consequently there is no appreciable flow of electricity between the battery terminals.

Certain materials occupy an intermediate position, between conductors and insulators, in the ability to pass an electric current. For this reason they are termed *semi-conductors*. Germanium and silicon are two such semi-conductors which are now very widely used in electronics. The semi-conducting properties of such materials may again be explained by the behaviour of the electrons in the atoms of the materials.

Atoms of germanium and silicon each have four electrons in their outer shells. The solid is held firmly together because each of these *valence* electrons is shared with a neighbouring atom so that all the atoms are held in the *crystal lattice* by *valence bonds*, each bond consisting of a pair of electrons shared by two atoms. Each atom is therefore held in the lattice by four such valence bonds. All the electrons in the outer shells are used to produce these bonds and are attached firmly to the lattice. However, when the solid is exposed to a form of energy, for example heat or light, a few electrons are liberated. They are free to move through the solid if a voltage (from a battery) is applied to it.

In a semi-conductor, there are always a moderate number of such 'free' electrons, far fewer than in a conductor, and these are responsible for the semi-conducting properties. When one electron is liberated it leaves behind a 'hole' in the lattice. Other electrons then have somewhere to go, and a conduction process with electrons passing from one atom to the next· is possible. Materials which become semi-conducting when their electrons receive energy in the form of heat or light are referred to as *intrinsic* semi-conductors. There are, however, other forms of semi-conductors, and these are the types which are used in semi-conductor diodes and transistors. These *impurity* semi-conductors are artificially produced by introducing minute quantities of other materials into the crystals of the semi-conductor.

Materials like arsenic, phosphorus and antimony have atoms which each have five valence electrons. If, then, one atom of arsenic is placed in the ger-

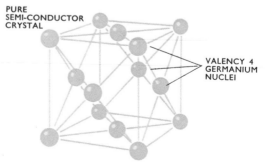

PURE SEMI-CONDUCTOR CRYSTAL

VALENCY 4 GERMANIUM NUCLEI

In a pure semi-conductor crystal (such as germanium) each atom is held in the lattice by four valence bonds shared with neighbouring atoms. Each bond is a shared pair of electrons.

SHARED ELECTRONS

SIDE-VIEW OF LATTICE

manium crystal lattice there will be one spare or *free* electron which cannot be bonded into the structure of the four adjacent germanium atoms. This free electron will move through the crystal lattice if a battery is connected across it. Such a material, with an added 'valence five' impurity, is known as an *n-type* semi-conductor, because the *majority carriers* (the free electrons) are negative. In such a material there would still be some charge carried by free electrons released by heat or light energy but this amount of flow would be very much smaller than that due to the impurity. The impurity atoms are known as *donors* because they *donate* an electron.

In a similar manner when one atom of a material such as indium, boron or gallium, whose atoms each have three valence electrons, is added to a crystal of germanium, there will be one incomplete valence bond in the structure of three germanium atoms and one impurity atom. There will then be an unfilled 'hole' in the basic valence structure of the material.

If a free electron in the solid were to move into this hole to make up the full set of valence bonds, then the atom from which the electron was lost will be positively charged because the *loss* of the

negative electron is the same as *gaining* a single *positive* charge. This means that a 'positive hole' has been created in the lattice. If another free electron fills the positive hole, then the vacancy due to the removal of the free electron creates yet another positive hole. In this way, the holes move through the conductor in an opposite direction from that of the electrons which create them, from the positive terminal to the negative terminal. Such a material, with an added 'valence three' impurity, is known as a

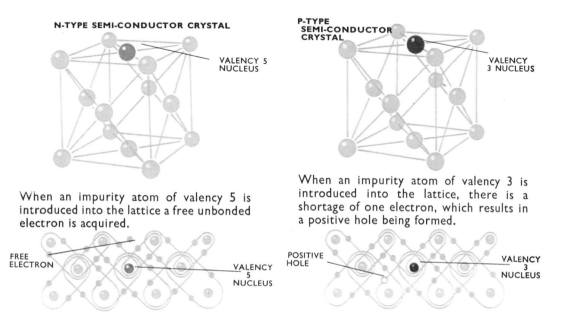

N-TYPE SEMI-CONDUCTOR CRYSTAL

VALENCY 5 NUCLEUS

When an impurity atom of valency 5 is introduced into the lattice a free unbonded electron is acquired.

FREE ELECTRON

VALENCY 5 NUCLEUS

P-TYPE SEMI-CONDUCTOR CRYSTAL

VALENCY 3 NUCLEUS

When an impurity atom of valency 3 is introduced into the lattice, there is a shortage of one electron, which results in a positive hole being formed.

POSITIVE HOLE

VALENCY 3 NUCLEUS

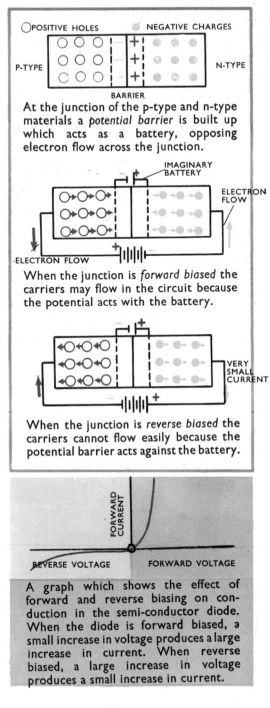

At the junction of the p-type and n-type materials a *potential barrier* is built up which acts as a battery, opposing electron flow across the junction.

When the junction is *forward biased* the carriers may flow in the circuit because the potential acts with the battery.

When the junction is *reverse biased* the carriers cannot flow easily because the potential barrier acts against the battery.

A graph which shows the effect of forward and reverse biasing on conduction in the semi-conductor diode. When the diode is forward biased, a small increase in voltage produces a large increase in current. When reverse biased, a large increase in voltage produces a small increase in current.

p-type semi-conductor as the majority of charge carriers (the holes) is positive. The impurity atoms here are termed *acceptors*.

It must be remembered that although there are free electrons in the n-type material, and positive holes in the p-type material, both of these materials are still electrically neutral with the charge on each electron, 'free' or 'bound', equalled by a positive charge on an atomic nucleus in the lattice.

p-n Junctions

If a piece of p-type semi-conductor is very closely joined to a piece of n-type it might at first be supposed that the free electrons from the n-type would immediately cross the junction of the two pieces and 'fill' the vacant holes in the p-type piece of material. Although this recombination process does occur it takes place only for a very short time; it is stopped by a build-up of positive charge on the n-type side of the junction and a build-up of negative charge on the p-type side of the junction. This is due to the fact that the transfer of an electron from the n-type material gives a negative charge to the previously neutral p-type material, leaving the n-type material short of one negative charge, and therefore positive. The build up of charge on either side of the junction is rather like erecting a barrier to the flow.

When a battery is connected across the ends of the two pieces of semi-conductor so as to oppose this barrier, the balance of forces at the junction is upset. Free electrons in the n-type piece are repelled by the cathode of the battery and are therefore forced towards the junction and through the barrier; similarly, holes in the p-type piece are repelled by the positively charged anode of the battery and are therefore forced towards the junction and through the barrier. As the battery *voltage* (electrical pressure) is increased, more and more free electrons and holes are forced across the junction and through the barrier. When a battery is connected to a p-n junction in this way, the junction is said to be *forward biased.*

When the connections are reversed, the battery is said to be *reverse biased.* The effect of battery voltage is now acting in the same direction as the barrier effect and so there is no flow of current. As the battery voltage is increased a small flow of current takes place because there are always a few charge carriers which have sufficient energy to overcome the potential barrier. This *reverse* current is thousands of times smaller than the *forward* current for the same size of battery voltage.

A p-n junction acts in a similar manner to a thermionic diode in that it offers a relatively easy conducting path (i.e. a low electrical resistance) to current flow when the diode is forward biased, and a very poor conducting path (or high electrical resistance) to current flow when the diode is reverse biased. This has led to very wide use of semi-conducting diodes in electronics. Apart from being small and compact they have the great advantage over thermionic diodes in that they do not have heated cathodes, which means that a heater circuit does not have to be used in the equipment.

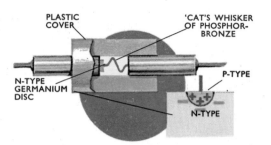

The point contact semi-conductor diode was made before the junction type. A 'cat's whisker' wire presses against a disc of n-type germanium. During manufacture, a relatively large current is passed through the 'point contact'; this has the effect of forming a zone of p-type germanium at the point contact. A p-n junction has been formed.

THE CRYSTAL DETECTOR

No one knows who gave the cat-whisker its name. But in 1910 this small, springy piece of metal made its first appearance in a radio receiver. The cat-whisker (or cat's whisker) was used to

A cat-whisker crystal detector. This form of detector needed constant readjustment—hence the pivot on the left. Only parts of the crystal's surface had detecting (rectifying) properties. The crystal was probed with the cat-whisker until sound could be detected from the earphones.

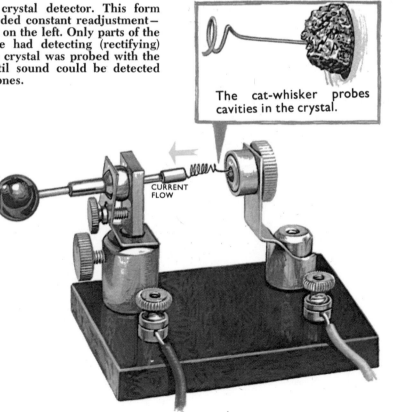

The cat-whisker probes cavities in the crystal.

probe minute cavities in the structure of a crystal of the mineral *galena*—the crystal in the well-known *crystal set*. Crystals were already used in radio sets to detect radio waves. In 1908 the crystal detector was a blunt piece of metal pressing into a galena crystal. A year or so later the detector took the form of two crystals pressing against each other.

The man who, in 1910, invented the cat-whisker was an American naval radio operator named Ben Miessner. He curled a pointed piece of metal cut from a copper sheet into a crude spring, and mounted the metal on a rod so that it could be moved to and fro to make contact with the fixed crystal. He connected a radio aerial, a coil and tuning capacitor to one side of the crystal, and a pair of earphones to the cat-whisker side. His new kind of radio-wave detector turned out to be much more sensitive and reliable than previous crystal detectors. It was cheap, easy to make, and proved very popular. Most of the listeners in the early days of radio broadcasting heard their first programmes through a pair of earphones and a cat-whisker crystal set. The name cat-whisker first appeared in 1914, and stayed.

At their point of contact, the crystal and cat-whisker together make a signal *rectifier*. This allows current to pass through it in one direction only, from the crystal to the cat-whisker. The signal arriving at the crystal from the aerial is a high frequency *(radio-frequency)* wave modulated by a lower frequency *(audio-frequency)* wave. The audio-component defines the shape, or *envelope*, of the radio-frequency wave.

The radio-frequency wave oscillates too rapidly to produce an audible sound in a pair of earphones. Even the audio-frequency variations produce no audible sound, because a large current 'push' is immediately followed, at radio frequency, by an equally large 'pull' in the opposite direction. Pushes and pulls cancel each other out.

The crystal detector lets through only the current 'pushes'. The 'pulls' are held back, they do not cancel out the pushes and the resultant signal can produce sound in a pair of earphones.

The detection stage is the key process in all radio receivers. (The signal detector is always a signal *rectifier*.) The amplifying stages, the smoothing components, the tone controls, the batteries and the additional components used in modern radio receivers are all refinements, to improve the quality of the sound, and give the signal enough power to operate a loudspeaker. The bare essentials are the aerial, the tuner, the detector and the earphones.

Not all crystals can rectify currents when they are attached to a cat-whisker. Galena will do it, but only on certain points of its surface. The fine wire at the end of the cat-whisker is used to probe the surface, and find the spots which will work as rectifiers. Silicon, and carborundum with a springy-steel cat-whisker, were both used in early cat-whisker sets. The cat-whisker was

Diodes

The point-contact and junction germanium diodes are developments of the cat-whisker.

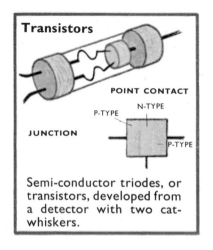

Transistors

Semi-conductor triodes, or transistors, developed from a detector with two cat-whiskers.

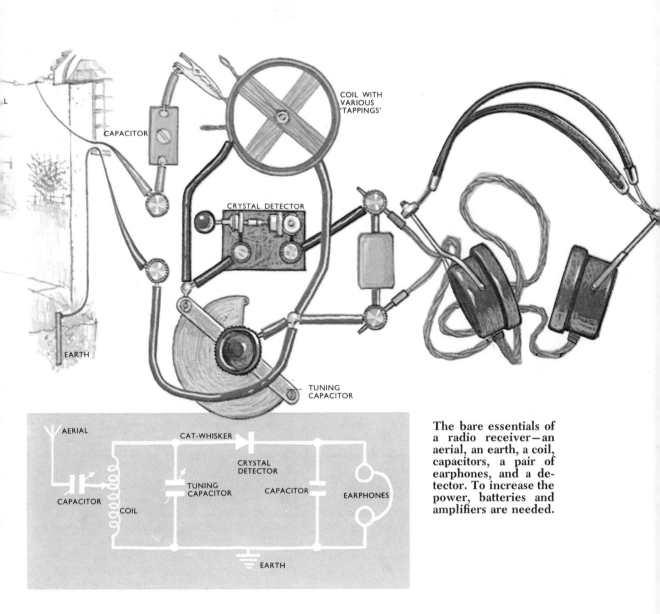

Labels in illustration:
COIL WITH VARIOUS 'TAPPINGS'

CAPACITOR

CRYSTAL DETECTOR

EARTH

TUNING CAPACITOR

AERIAL

CAT-WHISKER

CRYSTAL DETECTOR

CAPACITOR

COIL

TUNING CAPACITOR

CAPACITOR

EARPHONES

EARTH

The bare essentials of a radio receiver—an aerial, an earth, a coil, capacitors, a pair of earphones, and a detector. To increase the power, batteries and amplifiers are needed.

finely balanced, and needed constant re-adjustment.

Nowadays more reliable forms of crystal detector are available. The crystal used is the semi-conductor *germanium*. *Point-contact* germanium detectors, or germanium *diodes*, are very similar to the original cat-whisker and crystal. The great improvement is that the cat-whisker is embedded permanently in the crystal. It does not need adjusting.

But the majority of modern germanium diodes are made differently. They are called *junction* diodes. They do the same job of rectification and detection but more efficiently than the point-contact diode.

The springy cat-whisker is replaced by another piece of germanium. A different kind of impurity is added to each piece of germanium, giving each different arrangements of electrical charges within the crystal. At the *junction*, where the two pieces are fused together, the electrical charges interact with each other to produce a kind of electrical barrier. This stops an electric current (a flow of negatively charged electrons) from passing through the junction in one direction, but does nothing to stop them in the other direction.

All kinds of solid rectifier, whether

they are made of galena, silicon, carborundum or germanium work as a result of electrical interactions on an atomic level. In the original cat-whisker, the difference in electrical arrangement between the atoms in the galena and the cat-whisker metal was sufficient to build a one-way 'barrier'. In a germanium junction diode, the 'barrier' is much more pronounced, and the diode is therefore more efficient as a rectifier.

During the 1930's, the crystal detector gradually went out of favour, as it was superseded by the *diode valve* detector. This is a *thermionic* valve, and it rectifies current by an entirely different principle. Thermionic valves—triodes, tetrodes and pentodes—were used in the amplifying stages of the radio sets, which became much bulkier.

The interesting properties of crystals were not, however, forgotten. Radar was developing, and the thermionic diode could not operate at the very high frequencies used in radar. Electrically it was too bulky—its *capacitance* was too large. The point-contact diode could be used at very high frequencies, because its electrical capacitance was so minute. The area of contact, which gives rise to capacitance, is very small indeed.

It was in this period also that the Russian scientist Losev, working in Nizhni Novgorod, stuck two cat-whiskers in a single crystal. He had produced the first solid-state sandwich, the forerunner of the modern transistor.

With two cat-whiskers, even more control could be exercised over the electric currents flowing through the device. It could be operated as a one-way valve, an ON/OFF switch, or as an *amplifier*. Again, the properties could be explained by the electrical 'barrier' effects when two dissimilar pieces of solid material are in contact. There are two separate barriers in a transistor. But an additional electrical lead, connected to the middle part of the sandwich, in the crystal itself, is necessary. This middle region is vital to the current control.

Losev's transistor prototype was a *point-contact* transistor. As the junction diode is more efficient than the point-contact diode, so the junction transistor is more efficient than the point-contact

transistor. The junction transistor was discovered in 1948 by three scientists, Shockley, Bardeen and Brittain, working at the Bell Telephone Laboratories.

The two kinds of semi-conducting germanium or silicon used for the transistor are called *n-type* and *p-type*. N-type contains an impurity which frees negative charges (electrons) in the solid crystal. P-type impurity frees positive charges (electron deficits). A transistor is either an n-type/p-type/n-type sandwich or a p-type/n-type/p-type sandwich. Both work equally well. At present the p/n/p variety is easier to manufacture, but with new manufacturing techniques this need not always be so.

At each junction is developed an electrical barrier, either increased or diminished by connecting batteries to the transistor. In one method of using the transistor, the electron gains enough energy at a tiny barrier to pass over a much larger barrier. Each barrier is really a difference in electrical voltage (or potential). A small voltage change is turned into a much bigger voltage change, so this kind of transistor operates as a *voltage amplifier*.

The transistor is, however, usually used in a different way, as a *current amplifier*. This makes use of the most sensitive region in the transistor, the very thin piece of semiconductor sandwiched in the middle between the two electrical barriers. A very small current (the signal which needs amplifying) fed into this region can easily block the region, by neutralizing the free electric charges which would otherwise carry current through the transistor from one of the sandwiches to the other. A small change can cause a much larger change in current, so the device is a current amplifier (it also gets some *voltage amplification* from the two barriers).

Many variations of the transistor have since been made. The original junction transistors could not be used at very high frequencies, because the current carriers took too long to diffuse their way through the middle region. In the latest transistors, the region between the junction is very small indeed, and they can be used at frequencies of a few thousand million cycles per second.

The Junction Transistor

WHEN a piece of silicon or germanium crystal is 'doped' with a very small quantity of a *donor* element such as phosphorus or arsenic, an *n-type* semi-conductor is formed. When the same material is doped with an *acceptor* element such as indium or boron, a *p-type* semi-conductor is formed. The n-type semi-conductor contains a number of free electrons, whilst the p-type semi-conductor contains a number of free positive 'holes', caused by the lack of a sufficient number of electrons to fill the valence bonds in the lattice of the crystal.

If a p-type material is joined to an n-type material then a device which acts like a *diode* valve is formed. If a very thin piece of n-type material is sandwiched between two pieces of p-type material, or a very thin piece of p-type material is sandwiched between two pieces of n-type material, a *junction transistor* is formed. The former arrangement is called a *p-n-p* junction transis-

Cross-section of a typical junction transistor showing the thin *base* layer of a semi-conductor sandwiched between the *collector* and *emitter* layers.

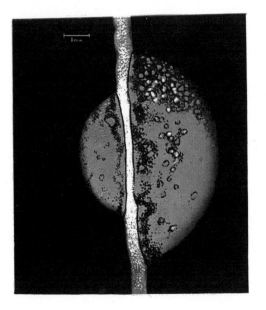

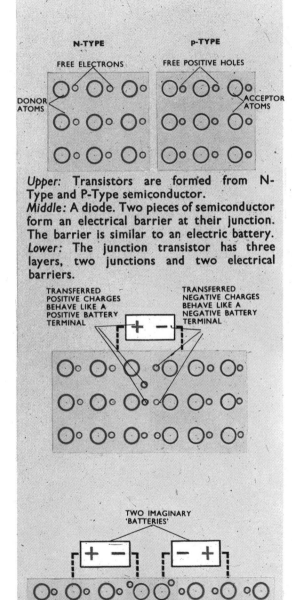

Upper: Transistors are formed from N-Type and P-Type semiconductor.
Middle: A diode. Two pieces of semiconductor form an electrical barrier at their junction. The barrier is similar to an electric battery.
Lower: The junction transistor has three layers, two junctions and two electrical barriers.

In an n-p-n junction transistor, one n-type layer is called the *emitter* and the other the *collector*. The p-type layer is called the *base*. When an external battery is connected between the emitter and base, free electrons in the emitter are repelled by the negative terminal and are driven into the base. Here, a few of the electrons combine with a few of the positive holes, but the base is very thin and the number of holes in it is made to be small. So practically all of the electrons pass on across the second junction.

There is opposition to the flow of electrons across the junction between emitter and base, but this is small because the way in which the imaginary 'battery' is connected *assists* the external battery. This form of connection of the external battery is called *forward biassing*.

At the junction between the base and collector, the imaginary battery *opposes* the passage of electrons, since it is connected the opposite way round to the external battery. This junction is then *reverse biassed.*

However, the second external battery assists the first external battery in driving the electrons through the second junction, because the two batteries are connected in series. In fact, about 98% of all the electrons leaving the emitter arrive at the collector.

The overall effect of connecting the two external batteries to the junction transistor is to force the electrons from emitter to collector over two barriers, one after the other. The first barrier (being forward biassed) is a small one. The second barrier (being reverse biassed) is a much larger one. The *current* passing through both junctions is, however, pretty well the same.

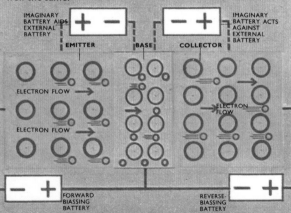

The action of the n-p-n junction transistor may be compared with a jet of water from a hose-pipe.

If the jet is very powerful it may be assumed that it travels in a straight line, unaffected by gravity. If the jet is directed to clear a rope barrier at A, and then another higher one at B, it will hit the wall at the point C. The jet is driven by the pressure of the water in the hose, and the amount of water arriving at C is nearly equal to that leaving the hose.

In the transistor, the electron current is driven by the electrical 'pressure' (voltage) obtained from the external batteries over a small barrier at the first junction and a much larger barrier at the second junction. Most of the current leaving the emitter arrives at the collector.

THE FIRST ROPE BARRIER IS MUCH NEARER AND LOWER THAN THE SECOND ONE

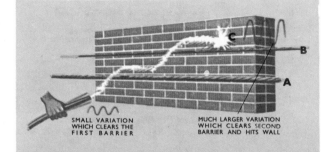

SMALL VARIATION WHICH CLEARS THE FIRST BARRIER

MUCH LARGER VARIATION WHICH CLEARS SECOND BARRIER AND HITS WALL

If now, the hose-jet is moved up and down a small amount but still directed so as to clear the rope barriers at A and B, quite a small movement of the hose-end is translated into a very large movement of the jet at the wall. The amount of water leaving the hose is once again almost the same as the amount arriving at the wall.

Similarly, in a transistor, a small change in voltage between emitter and base (the 'hose' end) is *amplified* into a large change in voltage between the collector and base (the 'wall' end). The current is unchanged.

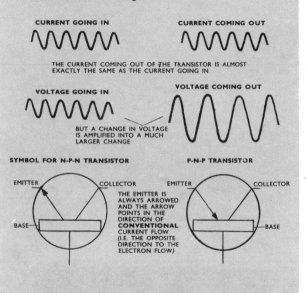

Both n-p-n and p-n-p transistors are used to amplify voltages. Since the p-n-p is the more usual type, all transistors described in the following chapters are assumed to be p-n-p.

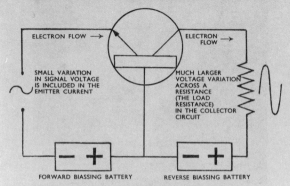

AN N-P-N VOLTAGE AMPLIFIER

tor, and the latter an *n-p-n* junction transistor.

Such transistors may be used in electronic circuits to carry out most of the functions of the ordinary thermionic triode valve.

THE COMMON EMITTER

In a transistor, a current travels through all three parts of the semiconductor 'sandwich'. It passes first through the *emitter*, then through the *base*, and out through the *collector*. Batteries can be connected to the transistor in such a way that an *electrical barrier* is set up at the junction between the base and collector. The barrier acts almost like a battery, increasing the *voltage* of any electrical signal fed in to the transistor. The transistor *amplifies* the voltage of an electrical signal.

When transistors were first discovered, it seemed logical to put the varying signal current in through the *emitter*. It was simply added to the normal operating current. This sort of transistor did not amplify the signal current because practically the same amount of current left via the collector as entered via the emitter. But, on the other hand, it amplified the *voltage* of the signal as it crossed the base/collector barrier. The amplification was about 100 if the transistor was connected in the right way.

Transistors are often likened to triode (three-electrode) valves. The emitter, base and collector of the transistor are similar to the cathode, grid and anode of a triode valve. Most often, in a valve circuit, the signal is put on to the *grid*. If the transistor is to function in the same sort of way, the signal should be fed into it via the base.

This is in fact the most usual method of using transistors. Circuits where the transistor is so connected are called *common emitter*, or alternatively *grounded emitter*, circuits.

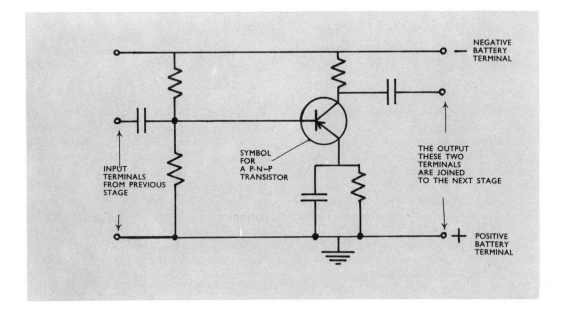

A typical circuit for an amplifying stage in an audio-frequency amplifier. This is a common emitter circuit, since the emitter is included in both input and output circuits. The two upper resistors are to set the base and collector currents (and in consequence, their voltages) at the right values. The lower two resistors and capacitor are the *bias stabilizing* part of the amplifier. These components stop the transistor from overheating. The capacitors to right and left are *coupling capacitors*. They join this circuit to others.

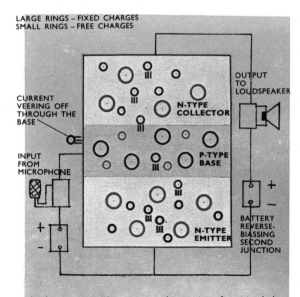

CURRENT
VEERING OFF
THROUGH THE
BASE

INPUT
FROM
MICROPHONE

OUTPUT
TO
LOUDSPEAKER

N-TYPE
COLLECTOR

P-TYPE
BASE

N-TYPE
EMITTER

BATTERY
REVERSE-
BIASSING
SECOND
JUNCTION

In the transistor there is a conglomeration of positive holes and negative charges, allied to fixed charges. Connecting the batteries in this way sends electrons through the transistor. Only one in 50 (2%) of the electrons combines with a 'positive hole' in the base, and goes out via the base. The existence of an electrostatic barrier between base and collector leads to amplification of voltage to positive.

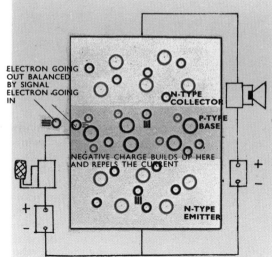

ELECTRON GOING
OUT BALANCED
BY SIGNAL
ELECTRON GOING
IN

N-TYPE
COLLECTOR

P-TYPE
BASE

NEGATIVE CHARGE BUILDS UP HERE
AND REPELS THE CURRENT

N-TYPE
EMITTER

Now stop the outward flow from the base. This is done by pumping in electrons (part of the electrical signal from the microphone) into the base to balance those going out. The 2% which normally combine with holes cannot now get out. The base rapidly becomes negatively charged and repels the incoming current. If 2% of the electrons from the emitter cannot get out, the other 98% are halted. A very small change in signal current is producing a change in output signal nearly 50 times larger.

The input signal is part of the current which flows through the emitter/base circuit. The output signal is part of the current which flows through the whole transistor—i.e. through emitter, base and collector. The emitter is the transistor part *common* to both input and output. The common part is usually connected to earth, and is said to be 'grounded'.

The main advantage of the common emitter is that the signal *current*, as well as the *voltage*, is amplified.

The signal current is put into the base of the transistor. At the instant when the signal current is nothing, 98% of the current flows straight through the base to the collector. Only 2% veers out through the base. This 2% controls the balance of positive and negative charges in the base, and it controls virtually the whole current flowing through the transistor. If the outflowing 2% is balanced by an equal *inflow of signal current* into the base, no net current flows out of the base. Negative charge rapidly builds up in the base, and repels the negatively charged electrons of the current. The current stops.

So by varying only 2% of the current, the other 98% can be controlled. This is equivalent to having a current amplification of 49. A small change in the base current causes a change 49 times bigger in the collector (output) current. The voltage of the signal is meanwhile being amplified up to 100 times at the barrier across the base/collector junction.

When the signal is fed in through the

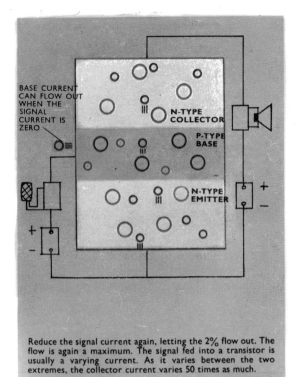

BASE CURRENT CAN FLOW OUT WHEN THE SIGNAL CURRENT IS ZERO

N-TYPE COLLECTOR

P-TYPE BASE

N-TYPE EMITTER

Reduce the signal current again, letting the 2% flow out. The flow is again a maximum. The signal fed into a transistor is usually a varying current. As it varies between the two extremes, the collector current varies 50 times as much.

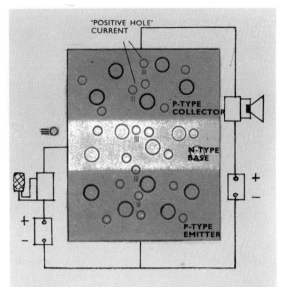

'POSITIVE HOLE' CURRENT

P-TYPE COLLECTOR

N-TYPE BASE

P-TYPE EMITTER

The p-n-p transistor has the same mode of operation. Battery terminals are switched around. The p-n-p is usually easier to make than the n-p-n transistor, and, mainly for this reason, is the kind used in most electronic circuits. However, it is slightly more confusing to explain. The current flows within the transistor as 'positive holes' in one direction while, in the connecting wires, the current is a stream of negative electrons in the opposite direction.

base (common emitter circuit), the total amplification (that is, of both current and voltage) is roughly 50 times greater than when the signal is fed in through the emitter (common base circuit).

This is a very much simplified picture of the happenings inside a transistor. The amplification it gives depends on the way it is connected into a circuit, and on the kind of signal.

A PRACTICAL AMPLIFIER

There are innumerable ways of connecting transistors in circuits and getting them to amplify electric signals. The circuit designer knows what kind of signal the circuit is to amplify, of what

frequency it is, and its size. He selects a transistor capable of dealing with this kind of signal. To the three transistor terminals, the *emitter*, the *base* and the *collector*, he connects resistors, capacitors or transformers. These have the job of regulating the voltages and currents supplied to the transistor.

Transistors operate at fairly low voltages. For example, the voltage between emitter and collector may be about 3 volts, and the battery needs supply to the circuit a total of only 6 volts.

The additional components around transistors fall roughly into three main types. First, there are the components needed to make sure that the right *direct currents* flow through the transistor. Two direct currents have to be set at their

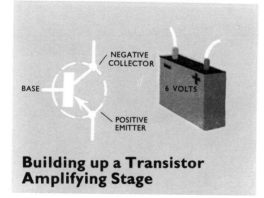

Building up a Transistor Amplifying Stage

The first two important parts are the transistor and the battery. This is a p-n-p transistor, and the arrow in the symbol goes into the transistor. The voltage difference between emitter and collector (for this particular transistor) should be about 3 volts. The arrow points in the direction of *conventional* current flow. The *electron* current flows in the opposite direction. It flows from negative to positive around the circuit, and the collector should therefore be more negative than the emitter.

correct values. There is the current which starts at the emitter and goes right through the transistor sandwich to the collector. Then there is the current which, instead of going from the emitter straight through the base (the middle part of the sandwich) to the collector, veers off through the base. Only about a fiftieth of the current from the emitter does this. The two currents are set at the

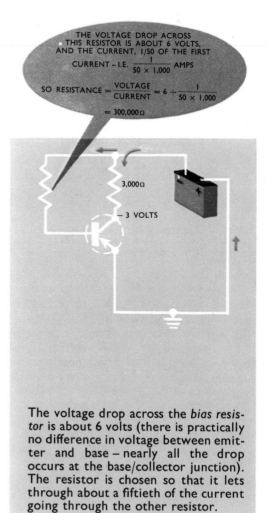

WHAT IS A LIKELY VALUE FOR THIS RESISTOR? THE CURRENT SHOULD BE ABOUT 1 MILLIAMP $\left(\frac{1}{1,000} \text{ AMP}\right)$

AND THE VOLTAGE DROP, 3 VOLTS SO FROM OHM'S LAW,

$$\text{RESISTANCE} = \frac{\text{VOLTAGE}}{\text{CURRENT}} = 3 \div \frac{1}{1,000}$$
$$= 3,000 \ \Omega \ (\text{OHMS})$$

THE VOLTAGE DROP ACROSS THIS RESISTOR IS ABOUT 6 VOLTS, AND THE CURRENT, 1/50 OF THE FIRST CURRENT – I.E. $\frac{1}{50 \times 1,000}$ AMPS

$$\text{SO RESISTANCE} = \frac{\text{VOLTAGE}}{\text{CURRENT}} = 6 \div \frac{1}{50 \times 1,000}$$
$$= 300,000 \ \Omega$$

The battery supplies 6 volts. This resistor, the *load* resistor, 'uses up' the extra 3 volts. The current through it (and through the transistor from emitter to collector) is about 1 milliamp.

The voltage drop across the *bias resistor* is about 6 volts (there is practically no difference in voltage between emitter and base – nearly all the drop occurs at the base/collector junction). The resistor is chosen so that it lets through about a fiftieth of the current going through the other resistor.

right values (which vary from transistor to transistor) by two resistors.

These components are used to set the *direct* current supplying the transistor. Another group of components deals with the *alternating* signal, feeding the signal into the transistor and taking it out after amplification.

Transistor amplifiers normally contain several transistors. One transistor circuit may be only one stage in the total amplifier. The alternating signal enters the transistor from the previous stage, and goes out of it into the next stage, probably to be amplified further. The connecting of one stage to another is called *coupling*, and, again, there are many ways of doing this.

The current from the previous stage is not a pure alternating signal. Instead, the signal is present as *variations* of the direct current going through the transistor. It therefore consists of two components, an *alternating* component, required by the next stage, and a *direct* current component, not required by the next stage. Usually *capacitors* form part of the coupling, since they allow alternating currents to pass through them, while stopping direct currents. Capacitors are used together with either resistors or *transformers* (two coils of wire, not actually touching but near each other so that the current in one induces a current in the other. One is part of the output of one stage, and the other part of the input of the next stage).

The third important part of the circuit,

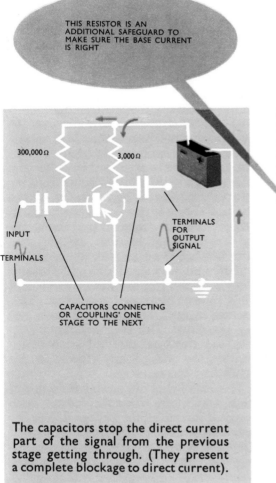

The capacitors stop the direct current part of the signal from the previous stage getting through. (They present a complete blockage to direct current).

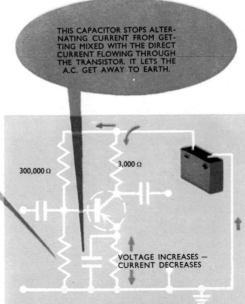

The current flowing through the transistor heats it. Heating may release electrons, and increase the emitter-to-collector current. Then more current flows through this resistor. From Ohm's Law, the voltage drop across it is larger. The battery supplies a maximum of 6 volts. When this resistance takes a larger share of the voltage, the voltage drop between emitter and collector is reduced. This automatically reduces the current, and irons out the heating increase.

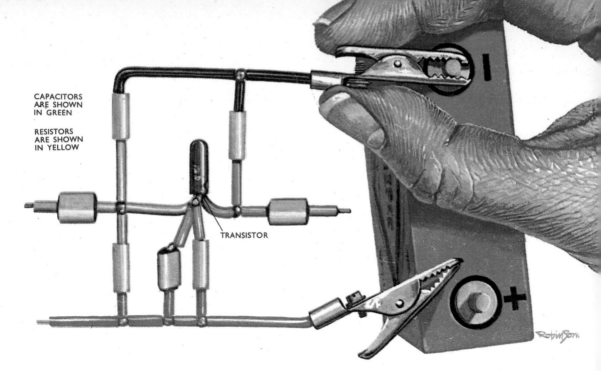

CAPACITORS
ARE SHOWN
IN GREEN

RESISTORS
ARE SHOWN
IN YELLOW

TRANSISTOR

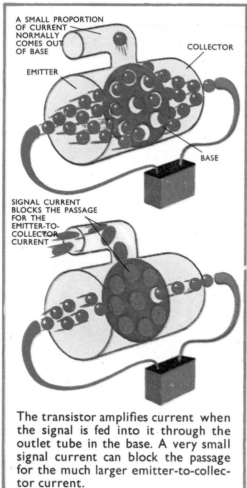

A SMALL PROPORTION
OF CURRENT
NORMALLY
COMES OUT
OF BASE

COLLECTOR

EMITTER

BASE

SIGNAL CURRENT
BLOCKS THE PASSAGE
FOR THE
EMITTER-TO-
COLLECTOR
CURRENT

The transistor amplifies current when the signal is fed into it through the outlet tube in the base. A very small signal current can block the passage for the much larger emitter-to-collector current.

The finished circuit, arranged as in the circuit diagram. In practice the arrangement of the components is far more compact.

which is almost indispensable in common emitter circuits (where the signal is fed into the transistor via the base), stops the transistor from overheating. A capacitor and resistor connected to the *emitter* act as *bias stabilizers*. Roughly this means that if the passage of the current through the transistor heats it, some 'fixed' electrons around the atoms in the transistor become unfixed, and pass through the transistor as an uncontrolled and unwanted electric current. They heat the transistor even more, and unfix more unwanted electrons. This process may 'avalanche' and burn out the transistor. The bias stabilizers stop this. As this uncontrolled current increases, the voltage drop across the bias stabilizers increases too.

The stabilizing circuit is connected in such a way that, when the voltage drop across it increases, the voltage difference between emitter and collector *decreases*. The difference in electric pressure pushing the current through the transistor decreases, the current is reduced, and so the increase in current through heating is immediately compensated.

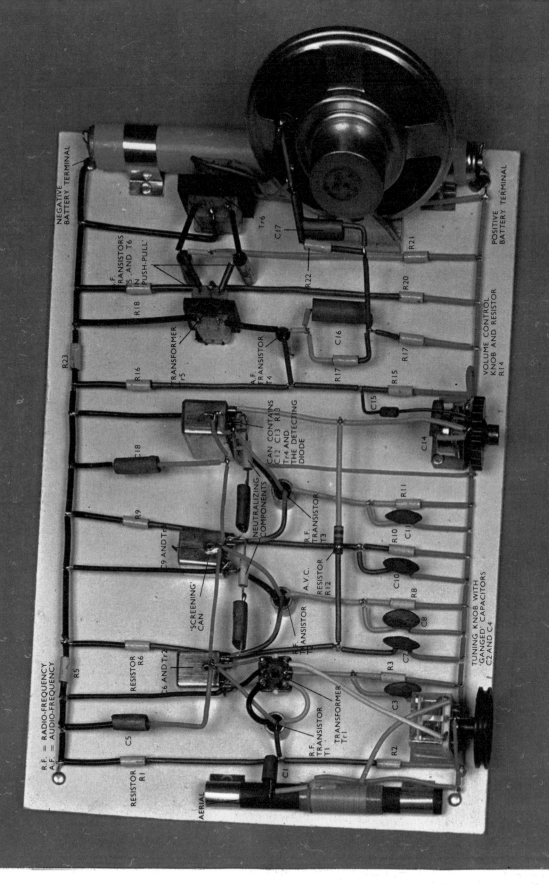

NEGATIVE BATTERY TERMINAL

POSITIVE BATTERY TERMINAL

Tr6

C17

R21

R22

R20

R.F. TRANSISTORS Tr5 AND Tr6 IN 'PUSH-PULL'

R18

R17

TRANSFORMER Tr5

A.F. TRANSISTOR Tr4

C16

R17

R15

R16

VOLUME CONTROL KNOB AND RESISTOR R14

R23

C15

C18

CAN CONTAINS C12 C13 R13 Tr4 AND THE DETECTING DIODE

C14

R9

NEUTRALIZING COMPONENTS

R.F. TRANSISTOR Tr3

R11

Tr9 AND Tr8

R10

C11

A.V.C. RESISTOR R12

C10

R8

'SCREENING' CAN

R.F. TRANSISTOR Tr2

C8

R5

RESISTOR R6

C7

Tr6 AND Tr2

R3

R.F. TRANSISTOR Tr1

TRANSFORMER Tr1

C3

R2

TUNING KNOB WITH 'GANGED' CAPACITORS C2 AND C4

C5

RESISTOR R1

R.F. TRANSISTOR T1

C1

AERIAL

R.F. = RADIO-FREQUENCY
A.F. = AUDIO-FREQUENCY

The Transistor Superhet-Receiver

WHEN it is finished, the transistor super-het radio receiver will fit into a box about 4 inches high, 6½ inches wide and 1½ inches deep. All the components will be soldered on to a printed circuit board, where most of the electrical connections between them will be made by the thin layer of copper deposited on to the back of the insulated board. But it is not easy to identify the properly assembled circuit with the circuit diagram.

For this reason, the model on the previous page has been made up simply by joining all the stages in order. An incoming radio signal starts at the aerial at one end, and finishes up as an audible sound at the loudspeaker at the other end.

Roughly speaking, the superhet can be divided into four stages. The aerial is part of the first stage, the *oscillating-mixing* stage, which is the key to the whole process of *heterodyning*. 'Superhet' stands for *super-heterodyne*, and heterodyning a signal means mixing it with another oscillating electrical signal of a higher frequency. This may seem to complicate matters inside the set, but in fact it is made to work so that it converts all radio signals, whatever their wavelength or frequency, into signals of *intermediate frequency*, of about 465 kilocycles per second. By doing this, the later stages of the set are simplified. Instead of having to deal with 'carrier' frequencies of anything from 500 kilocycles per second to 1,500 kilocycles per second, the later stages will have to allow through them only one kind of carrier signal, the 465 kilocycle signal.

In the second stage, the *intermediate frequency amplifiers* amplify the intermediate frequency radio signal. They are amplifying a signal of frequency 465 kilocycles per second, modulated or distorted by the information the signal is carrying. Transistors have to be designed specially to cope with the fairly high frequency, for the higher the frequency, the more difficult

it becomes to obtain a good amplification.

In particular, the transistors start behaving like capacitors at these frequencies, and to compensate for this, a *neutralizing circuit* has been added to the second stage of the model. Two resistors and two capacitors have the effect of cancelling out the capacitance of the transistors.

But while this circuit may be necessary for most transistors, it is not in fact required in this particular set. For there is something different about the first three transistors of the set. They have *four* leads instead of the customary three leading to base, collector and emitter. The red lead is the extra lead, and in common with all red wires on the circuit model, it leads directly to 'earth'. (It is usual for the positive 'red' terminal of the battery to be connected to 'earth' so that it is at 0 volts and the negative terminal of the 6 volt battery is at −6 volts.) By means of these earthed fourth connections, the effective capacitances of the transistors are reduced.

The intermediate frequency, 465 kilocycles per second, signal travels only as far as the end of the second stage, and is then disposed of. For the purpose of the third stage, the *diode detector*, is to separate the message from the intermediate frequency signal.

The diode lets through either the pushes of the alternating current, or the pulls, but not both. This enables the message part of the signal to have some effect, for before, when there were both pushes and pulls, the pushes and pulls were oscillating up and down at such a high frequency that pushes cancelled out pulls. If there are, for example, only pushes, then they cannot possibly cancel out with anything.

Still the signal contains some of the higher intermediate frequency. But only the lower frequency (audio frequency signal) is required. It is, however, a fairly simple matter to separate two

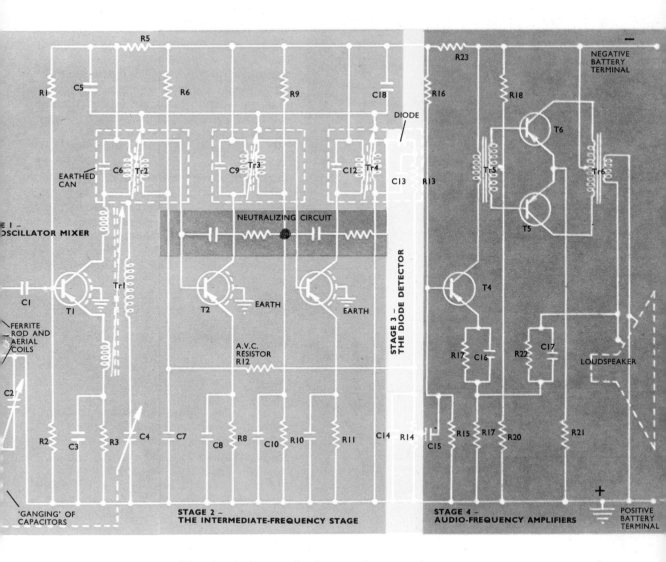

The circuit diagram for the complete superhet.

signals of different frequency. A capacitor, for instance, offers a fairly easy route to a high frequency signal. It does not offer such an easy path for a lower frequency signal. So the path of the signal branches, one branch leading to a capacitor and the other to a resistor. The intermediate frequency signal takes the capacitor route and the audio frequency signal takes the resistor route. The intermediate frequency signal finds it has been led along a blind alley, for the capacitor shunts it directly to Earth. However, the audio frequency signal chooses the path leading to the next stage.

The components lying between the third and fourth stages are of especial interest, for they include the volume control of the super-het set.

The volume control is basically a resistor, the second of the two branching resistors leading from the detecting stage. By altering the value of this resistor, the amount of signal reaching the next stage (and so the volume of the signal coming out of the set) can be controlled. An *automatic volume control* (A.V.C.) is also included. This is a resistor leading back from the end of the intermediate frequency part to the start

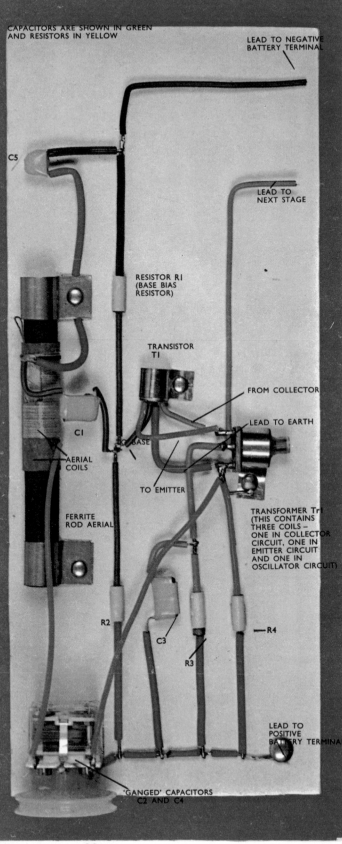

CAPACITORS ARE SHOWN IN GREEN AND RESISTORS IN YELLOW

LEAD TO NEGATIVE BATTERY TERMINAL

C5

LEAD TO NEXT STAGE

RESISTOR R1 (BASE BIAS RESISTOR)

TRANSISTOR T1

FROM COLLECTOR

LEAD TO EARTH

C1

TO BASE

AERIAL COILS

TO EMITTER

FERRITE ROD AERIAL

TRANSFORMER Tr1 (THIS CONTAINS THREE COILS – ONE IN COLLECTOR CIRCUIT, ONE IN EMITTER CIRCUIT AND ONE IN OSCILLATOR CIRCUIT)

R2

C3

R3

R4

LEAD TO POSITIVE BATTERY TERMINAL

'GANGED' CAPACITORS C2 AND C4

of the intermediate frequency part. It is sometimes known as a *feed-back* resistor, for it feeds back some of the signal across this stage. It has a sort of ironing out effect on the signal, reducing changes in the signal strength brought about by changes in atmospheric conditions.

In the fourth and final stage of the transistor, the signal is given its final *audio-frequency amplification*. The transistors amplify in their normal way in the first part of this stage, but in the second part of the stage, two transistors are employed to do the work of one. This arrangement has the advantage of drawing, on average, far less current from the battery.

The signal passes from these two transistors to a transformer, which transfers it across to the loudspeaker, where the signal at last becomes audible sound.

STAGE 1 — HETERODYNING THE SIGNAL

The radio signal reaching a radio aerial is an *electromagnetic wave*. It is a mixture of two different kinds of wave — the wave to be turned into the audible message, and the radio-frequency wave which carries the message. The radio wave vibrates up and down a few hundred thousand times each second (i.e. its *frequency* is a few hundred thousand cycles per second). The signal representing the audible message vibrates much more slowly (having a lower frequency of anything from 20 to 15,000 cycles per second).

At the aerial the waves are converted into surges of current. But there may be many different signals reaching the aerial from different transmitters, and the set must be capable of selecting just the one required. This means that it must be able to select a particular *radio-frequency*. It is found that the higher the frequency of the signal the more difficult it is to separate it from signals of similar

A model showing the components of the first stage, soldered onto a board for clarity to correspond with the circuit diagram (*right*).

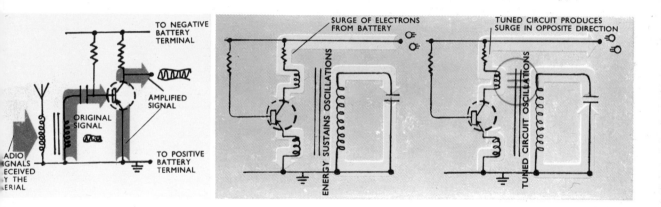

frequencies. The job of the *super-het* part of the super-het receiver is to make the separation easier by *lowering the frequency of the radio frequency part of the signal* (heterodyning). This is done in the first stage of the radio receiver.

The transistor amplifies the radio signal

The radio signal comes straight from the aerial, via a capacitor, to the base of the transistor. Just before it gets to the transistor, it meets the direct current coming down from the negative terminal of the battery into the base. In places, the radio signal current adds to the direct current, and in places it cancels it out. So the base current now becomes a varying current. The variations are amplified by the transistor, because the much larger current flowing from emitter to collector is very sensitive to changes in the base current.

The transistor feeds the oscillations

Amplification is just one of the things this transistor is doing. It is also helping to keep going electrical oscillations. These are the oscillations which are to be mixed with the radio signal, to *heterodyne* it.

As soon as the battery is connected, a surge of current flows from the negative battery terminal, down through the coil to the collector. The coil is in fact the primary coil of a transformer. The surge of current through the coil causes a rapid build-up of magnetic field around the coil, and the surge is passed, by

means of the rapidly changing magnetic fields linking the coils, to the secondary coil.

Current surges from the secondary coil to the capacitor in this circuit. Charge builds up on the capacitor plates, which shortly afterwards start to discharge again through the coil. Field builds up a second time around the coil and as it starts to die down again, a second surge of current rebuilds the charge on the capacitor plates. The current continues to surge to-and-fro from coil to capacitor — it is in fact oscillating with a particular frequency and the circuit is called a *tuned circuit*. The number of times the

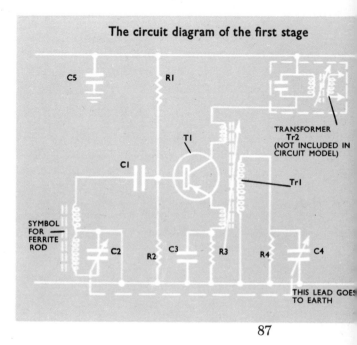

The circuit diagram of the first stage

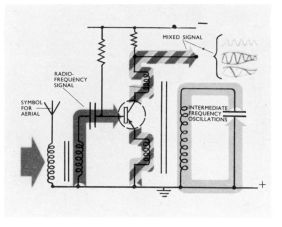

current surges to-and-fro each second (its frequency) is governed entirely by the *capacitance* of the capacitor and the *inductance* of the coil. The frequency in this radio set will be around 1,000,000 cycles per second (the usual frequency unit for this purpose is the kilo-cycle (kc) which is equal to one thousand cycles. So the frequency of the oscillations is around 1,000 kc/s).

If this were all that was happening, the oscillations would rapidly die down. Their surging to-and-fro around the circuit would stop because their energy would be eaten up in overcoming the resistance of the coil (no components can be made completely free from resistance).

But the coil of the tuned circuit is also linked with a coil leading to the emitter — in fact all three coils are wound together in the same transformer. The current surge which first appeared in the coil connected to the collector is now reflected into the emitter.

Signals entering the *emitter* of a transistor are automatically amplified. This is not quite like the current amplification of the signal entering the *base*. It is in fact amplified because of the peculiar effects of the electrostatic forces acting at the junctions between one part of the transistor sandwich and another part.

So as soon as the surge is received at the *emitter*, a much larger amplified surge passes through the coil connected to the *collector*. The transistor is effec-

tively pumping energy back into the tuned circuit, for it supplies this surge at just the right moment to sustain the oscillations within the tuned circuit.

The transistor mixes (heterodynes) two signals

Two oscillating currents are arriving at the transistor. One is the radio-frequency current reaching the base (its frequency is about 600 kc/s). The other is the oscillating current being pumped around the tuned circuit by the transistor. It goes right through the transistor, and its frequency is about 1,065 kc/s. The two oscillations are mixed in the transistor *(heterodyned)*, and the frequency (called the *intermediate frequency*) of the mixed signal is equal to the difference in frequency between the two signals. So its frequency is about 465 kc/s (1,065 − 600).

STAGE 2 — THE I.F. AMPLIFIERS

The tuning knob on a super-het radio receiver is connected to two variable capacitors. When the knob is twisted, the plates of the two capacitors are rotated

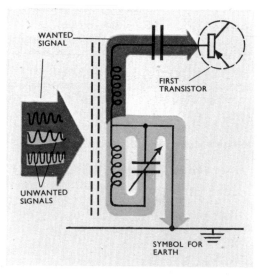

Tuning the Set
One radio signal is selected by adjusting a capacitor connected across part of the aerial circuit. Coil and capacitor form a tuned circuit designed to filter off all the unwanted signals to Earth.

88

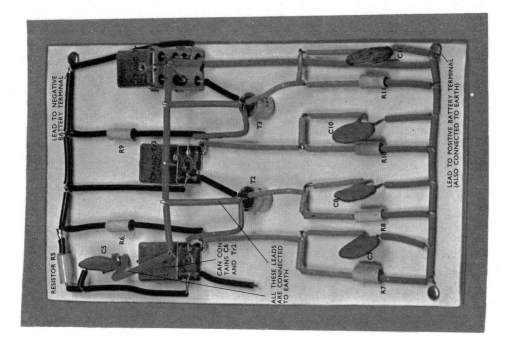

Labels visible in image: LEAD TO NEGATIVE BATTERY TERMINAL · R9 · RESISTOR R5 · C5 · R6 · CAN CONTAINS C6 AND Tr2 · ALL THESE LEADS ARE CONNECTED TO EARTH · T3 · T2 · C10 · R10 · C8 · C7 · R8 · R7 · C11 · R11 · LEAD TO POSITIVE BATTERY TERMINAL (ALSO CONNECTED TO EARTH)

together (they are said to be *ganged*), and the capacitance of both of them is altered at the same time. Each of the capacitors is a part of a *tuned circuit* – i.e. a circuit which responds far more to radio signals of a particular range of frequencies than to any other frequencies. By altering the capacitance of the tuning capacitors the frequency to which each tuned circuit responds (its *resonant* frequency) is altered.

Each radio programme is carried by radio waves of a certain frequency: so the required programme can be selected by twisting the tuning knob and varying the resonant frequencies of the two tuned circuits. The essential property of a *super-het* radio set is that the two tuned circuits are resonant at *two different frequencies*, differing by about 465 kilo-cycles per second (kc/s). If, for example, the incoming radio signal has a frequency of 1,265 kc/s, the first tuned circuit (connected to the aerial) will be resonant at 1,265 kc/s, while the second tuned circuit is oscillating at 800 kc/s. The difference in frequency is 465 kc/s (1,265−800). When the two signals are mixed together, or *hetero-dyned*, the mixture is a signal of a frequency equal to the difference in frequency between the two original

A model of the second stage of the transistor super-het, with the components arranged, for clarity, as in the circuit diagram on next page. In a real circuit the components are arranged differently, and the position of each is critical for good results to be achieved. For example, the lengths of connecting wires in some parts of the circuit must not be too great. Each of the metal cans contains a transformer and a tuning capacitor which comprise a tuned circuit. Each can is connected to earth as is the outer case of each transistor, to prevent outside interference from being 'picked up' and amplified in the succeeding stages.

signals. This is a consequence of the *interference* of radio waves of one frequency with waves of another frequency. The new, 465 kc/s signal is called the *intermediate frequency* signal, because its frequency is higher than the audio frequency signal (the actual information carried by the radio wave) and lower than the frequency of the original radio wave. The heterodyning step is carried out because the intermediate frequency

89

signal is easier to deal with in the subsequent stages of the transistor set.

Amplifying the intermediate frequency

From the first part of the super-het receiver the signal passes through two more transistors, which amplify it further. But the signal coming from the first stage contains three different signals —the original radio signal, the signal produced by the oscillator, and the intermediate frequency signal. Only the last of these is required. So the first stage is connected, or *coupled*, to the second stage by another tuned circuit, this one tuned to the intermediate frequency. So most of the intermediate frequency signal (and of course the audio frequency signal it is carrying) gets through to the base of the first transistor, while the proportion of the other two signals is very much reduced.

The signal enters the transistor through the base. By affecting the tiny base current (which flows into the transistor when no signal is being fed into it), the signal can cause much larger variations in the emitter-to-collector current. This is the amplified signal.

Connected to the collector of the transistor is yet another tuned circuit. Again, this circuit is designed to reduce the proportion of the radio and oscillator signals, while passing the intermediate frequency on to the next transistor amplifier. In the section shown in the

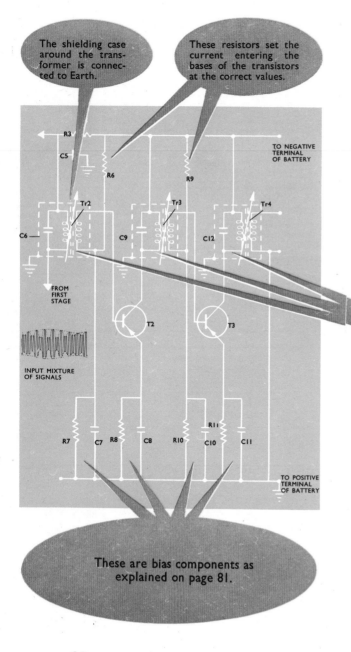

The shielding case around the transformer is connected to Earth.

These resistors set the current entering the bases of the transistors at the correct values.

These are tuned circuits for getting rid of unwanted parts of the signal. The coils of the tuned circuits are parts of the transformers, through which the signal is passed on to the next stage.

These are bias components as explained on page 81.

model on page 89, there are two transistors and three tuned circuits. As the signal passes through each transistor, it is amplified, and whenever one amplifier is connected to the next by a circuit tuned to the intermediate frequency (465 kc/s), signals of any frequency other than 465 kc/s are reduced in intensity. So by the time the signal gets to the end of this stage, it is very much larger and it consists of just the intermediate frequency, *modulated* by the audio-frequency signal.

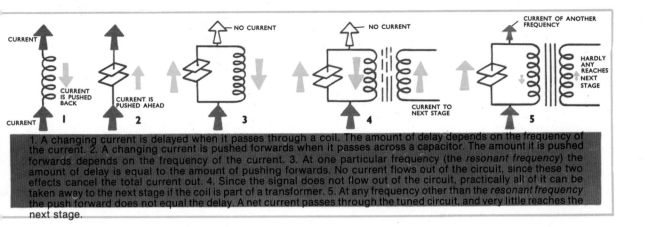

1. A changing current is delayed when it passes through a coil. The amount of delay depends on the frequency of the current. 2. A changing current is pushed forwards when it passes across a capacitor. The amount it is pushed forwards depends on the frequency of the current. 3. At one particular frequency (the *resonant frequency*) the amount of delay is equal to the amount of pushing forwards. No current flows out of the circuit, since these two effects cancel the total current out. 4. Since the signal does not flow out of the circuit, practically all of it can be taken away to the next stage if the coil is part of a transformer. 5. At any frequency other than the *resonant frequency* the push forward does not equal the delay. A net current passes through the tuned circuit, and very little reaches the next stage.

In the next stage these two signals will be separated.

STAGE 3—DETECTING THE SIGNAL

A diode is an electronic component which conducts electricity in one direction only. In the transistor super-het radio set there is just one diode, and this is the component which is said to *detect* the signal. The diode is to finally sort out the wanted 'message' part of the signal from the unwanted higher frequency signals associated with it. It is usual in transistor sets to use *semiconductor* diodes, and this set is no exception.

The diode was actually present in the model of the second stage of the transistor super-het, but then it was hidden inside a metal case 'screening' some of the components. In the model on page 93 the case has been removed to reveal one transformer, two capacitors, one resistor and the diode.

The transformer and one of the capacitors marked the end-point of the second stage, where the wanted 'message' signal and a signal of frequency 465 kilocycles per second were amplified together. The capacitor and the coils of the transformer form a *tuned circuit*, which responds to signals of frequency 465 kilocycles per second far more readily than to signals of any other frequency. It passes this signal on to the third stage.

It must be remembered that the wan-ted signal is what is called *amplitude modulating* the 465 kilocycle per second signal. The hearable *audio-frequency* defines the overall shape, or *envelope* of the higher-frequency signal. But it can be seen from the diagram on page 92 that the shape is symmetrical. 'Above the line' current 'pulls' are exactly balanced by 'below the line' current 'pushes'. 'Push' cancels 'pull' so the net effect is zero. The diode allows through it *either* 'pushes', or 'pulls', but *not* both. If, say, it is connected so that it allows through only current 'pushes' then the current coming out of the diode will consist of forward

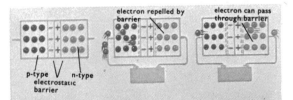

While the transistor itself is a sandwich of three parts of semiconducting material – either n-type/p-type/n-type or p-type/n-type/p-type, the semi-conductor diode is made from only two pieces of semi-conductor. It consists of a piece of n-type joined to a piece of p-type semi-conductor. A stream of electrons can flow from n-type to p-type, but not in the opposite direction. This is the result of adding a few impurity atoms to the originally pure pieces of semi-conductor. In n-type semi-conductor, extra free negative charges have been added, while the impurity atoms in p-type have added to it extra free positive charges.

When the two types are joined together positive charges flow in one direction across the junction, and negative charges in the other direction. The flow soon stops, but it has formed a 'barrier' of electrostatic force which will repel a current of electrons approaching it from the wrong direction.

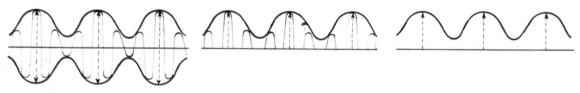

The diode removes half of the signal (2). By the time the signal reaches the next stage, all the higher frequency part has disappeared (3).

'pushes' of varying size. The size, or *amplitude* of the 'push' determines the eventual volume of the signal. The rate at which the current pushes to-and-fro determines the frequency, or pitch, of the sound coming out of the radio set.

The diode, however, does not get rid of the 465 kilocycle per second signal, now unwanted because if it is further amplified, it might distort the audio-frequency signal. But the resistor and

the second of the capacitors uncovered by removing the screening case are included to, in effect, filter away the 465 kilocycle per second signal. The signal coming from the diode is faced with a choice of two alternative routes. It can flow either through a resistor, or through a capacitor. The higher the frequency of an alternating electric current, the more it prefers to travel through a capacitor. So most of the 465 kilocycle per second

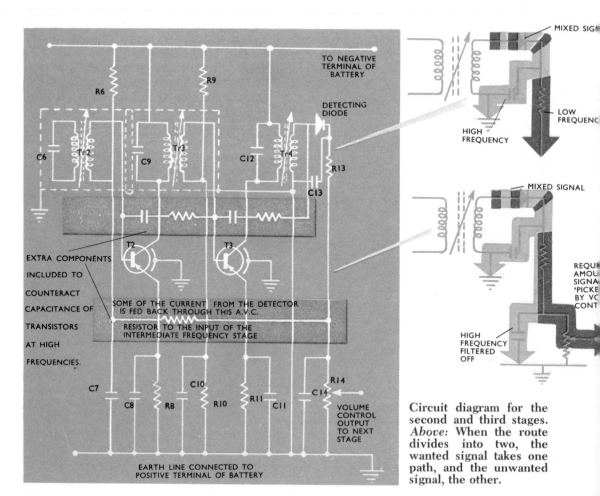

Circuit diagram for the second and third stages. *Above:* When the route divides into two, the wanted signal takes one path, and the unwanted signal, the other.

signal takes the capacitor route, which 'shunts' it away to Earth, while most of the lower audio-frequency signal goes on to the next stage via the resistor.

As this does not usually separate the signals sufficiently, the path is again divided into two parts, a capacitor route and a resistor route. Most of the remaining 465 kilocycle per second signal chooses the 'blind alley' route through the capacitor to Earth. The rest of the signal, which is by now nearly all audio-frequency, and very little 465 kilocycle per second frequency, goes on to the fourth stage of the transistor set, the *audio-frequency amplifier*.

Automatic Volume Control, or A.V.C.

The knob which controls the final volume of sound delivered by the radio set is also included in the third stage. The volume control is an adjustable resistor, and it is, in fact, the second of the resistors forming the 'alternative routes' leading from the detector diode. The first resistor is chosen so that the wanted current flows through it. But, if the set is to produce any volume of sound at all, the signal has to be discouraged from flowing through the second, volume-control resistor. Instead, it must flow on to the base of the first transistor in the next amplifying stage. When the volume control resistance is small, the volume of sound will be small, for a large proportion of the signal has found it easier to take the small-resistance path through the volume control. This leads it away to Earth. When the volume control knob is turned so that the volume control resistance is large, then very little of the signal will prefer to travel through it to Earth. Most of it prefers to take the route through to the amplifying stage, so the resulting sound volume will be large.

When the volume control resistance is large, the volume of sound is large. When the volume control resistance is small, the sound volume is low.

However, other, uncontrollable factors may also be affecting the volume of the signal. Atmospheric conditions, in particular, may affect the strength of the signal received by the radio aerial. An *automatic volume control* automatically compensates for these random increases

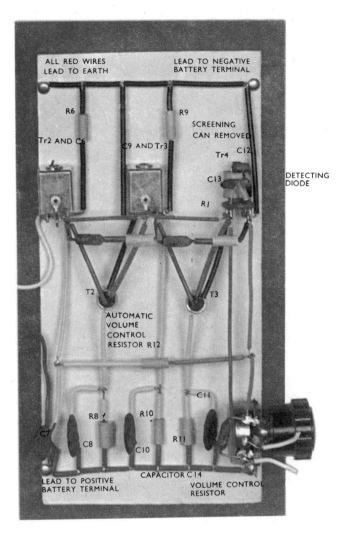

Model of the second and third stages of the superhet.

and decreases in the signal strength. The automatic volume control in this radio set is simply one resistor, connected between the output end of the diode detector and leading back to the input end of the previous stage, the *intermediate frequency amplifier*. It is principally to include the automatic volume control that the circuit model for the third stage includes all the components of the previous stage.

By connecting just this one resistor, the current from the detector is given another possible route. But this route takes it back one stage, i.e. it feeds it

93

back through the amplifying stage again. It leads to the base of the first transistor. When uncontrollable factors have made the volume large, the amount of current 'fed back' is relatively large. This current is, however, going in the opposite direction, through the transistor, to the direct current 'biassing' the transistor. So there is a net reduction in the current going through the transistor, and this has the effect of reducing the amplification it gives.

Slow changes in volume inflicted on the signal by atmospheric conditions are smoothed out. If a large signal appears, then a fraction of it is 'fed back' through the resistor so that it is amplified less.

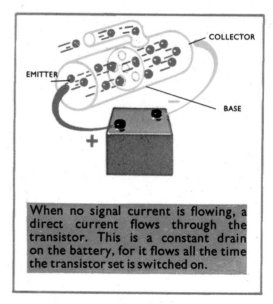

When no signal current is flowing, a direct current flows through the transistor. This is a constant drain on the battery, for it flows all the time the transistor set is switched on.

STAGE 4—THE AUDIO FREQUENCY AMPLIFIER

By the time the radio signal has gone through the first four stages of the transistor set, all that remains is the wanted 'message' part of the signal. Already the signal has passed from the aerial through three transistors, where it has been 'mixed', or *heterodyned* and amplified. Then it passed through a semi-conductor diode and was 'detected' so that the wanted audio frequency part was turned into to-and-fro surges of

current, moving to-and-fro at an audio frequency. (Audio, or hearable frequencies range from 20 cycles per second to 15,000 cycles per second.)

Not until now is the signal capable of producing an audible sound when it is fed into a loudspeaker. But if the signal as it now stands were fed into a loudspeaker, it would produce very little sound at all. It needs amplifying further, and this is the job done by the fourth stage of the super-het.

The further amplification is done in two parts, one transistor being used in the first part, and two in the second. These transistors are of a different type from the transistors used in previous stages, which had to cope with high frequency signals.

On entering the base of the first transistor, the signal current either blocks or frees the route through the transistor, from emitter to collector. *As a much larger direct* current is normally being pushed through the transistor (by the battery), just a tiny current alternately blocking and freeing the route from emitter to collector can cause considerable variations in the much larger current. In other words, the small signal current variations are *amplified* into much larger variations.

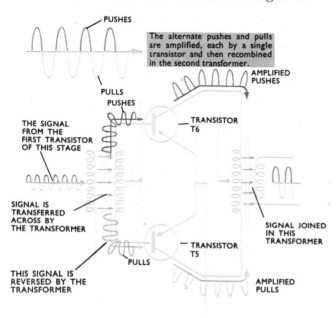

PUSHES

The alternate pushes and pulls are amplified, each by a single transistor and then recombined in the second transformer.

AMPLIFIED PUSHES

PULLS
PUSHES
PUSHES

THE SIGNAL FROM THE FIRST TRANSISTOR OF THIS STAGE

TRANSISTOR T6

SIGNAL IS TRANSFERRED ACROSS BY THE TRANSFORMER

SIGNAL JOINED IN THIS TRANSFORMER

THIS SIGNAL IS REVERSED BY THE TRANSFORMER

TRANSISTOR T5

PULLS

AMPLIFIED PULLS

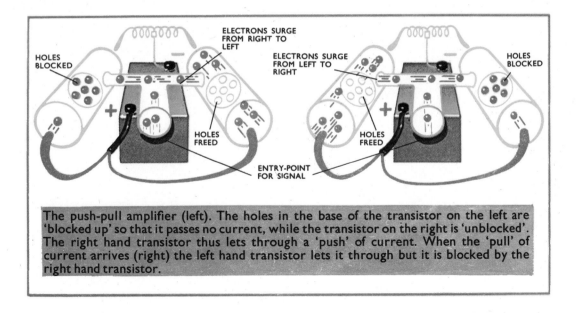

ELECTRONS SURGE FROM RIGHT TO LEFT

ELECTRONS SURGE FROM LEFT TO RIGHT

HOLES BLOCKED

HOLES BLOCKED

HOLES FREED

HOLES FREED

ENTRY-POINT FOR SIGNAL

The push-pull amplifier (left). The holes in the base of the transistor on the left are 'blocked up' so that it passes no current, while the transistor on the right is 'unblocked'. The right hand transistor thus lets through a 'push' of current. When the 'pull' of current arrives (right) the left hand transistor lets it through but it is blocked by the right hand transistor.

From this transistor, the signal goes on, via the collector, to the next pair of transistors.

Here the circuit arrangement is rather different. The two transistors are to do about the same amount of amplification as one transistor. While this may seem to be a waste of a transistor, there are good reasons for including an extra one.

The main reason is that it draws less current from the battery. In addition it works out to be more efficient when operating under full power. The signal is shared between the two transistors; one transistor amplifying the current 'pushes' and the other amplifying the current 'pulls'. Consequently the arrangement is called a *push-pull* amplifier.

As each transistor is dealing with only half the signal, a signal twice as large can be amplified without the unpleasant effects which accompany putting a large signal through a single transistor. A large signal may be distorted, and so much current may be flowing through the transistor that it overheats and 'burns out'. After they have been amplified, the two signals will be combined again and fed to the loudspeaker.

The signal is divided into two as follows. From the collector of the first transistor of this stage, the signal passes through a coil, which is in fact the *primary* coil of a transformer. The secondary transformer coil is divided exactly into two. When a current flows in the primary coil, it *induces* a current to flow in the secondary coil. The mid-point of this secondary is connected in such a way that the 'pushes' of the current go to one transistor (this is the current induced in one half of the secondary coil) while the current 'pulls' go to the other transistor. 'Pulls' and 'pushes' enter the bases of their respective transistors, and, as they did in previous stages of amplification, the small 'pushes' and 'pulls' cause much larger 'pushes' and 'pulls' in the current flowing through the transistor.

'Pushes' and 'pulls' are recombined. The combined current flows through another transformer coil, which is the primary coil of the final transformer, leading to the loudspeaker. The power necessary to operate the loudspeaker is transferred across to it through this transformer.

Combined signal currents *induce* currents in the loudspeaker coil. Because a current is flowing around the loudspeaker coil, it behaves like a magnet, and alternately attracts and repels another magnet in the loudspeaker. The

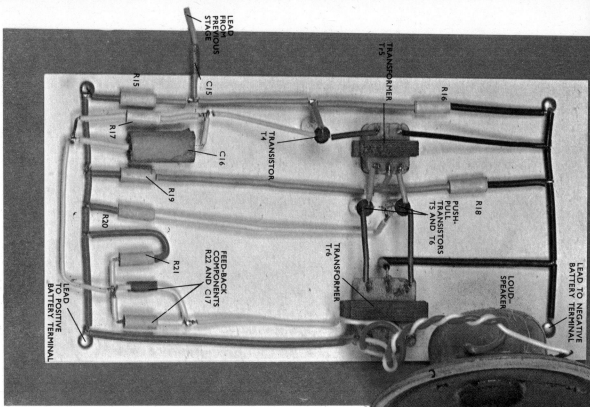

The fourth and final stage of the superhet.
The feedback components take some of the
signal back to the beginning of the stage.

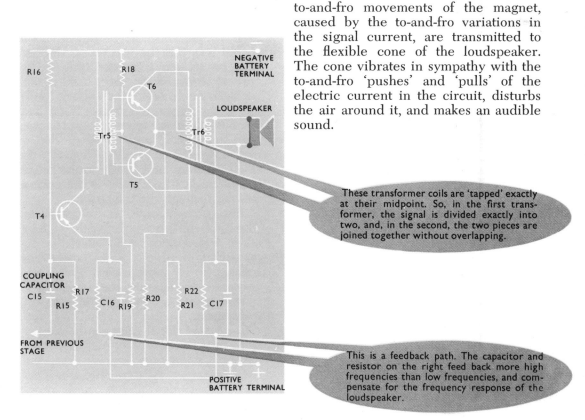

to-and-fro movements of the magnet,
caused by the to-and-fro variations in
the signal current, are transmitted to
the flexible cone of the loudspeaker.
The cone vibrates in sympathy with the
to-and-fro 'pushes' and 'pulls' of the
electric current in the circuit, disturbs
the air around it, and makes an audible
sound.

These transformer coils are 'tapped' exactly
at their midpoint. So, in the first transformer, the signal is divided exactly into
two, and, in the second, the two pieces are
joined together without overlapping.

This is a feedback path. The capacitor and
resistor on the right feed back more high
frequencies than low frequencies, and compensate for the frequency response of the
loudspeaker.

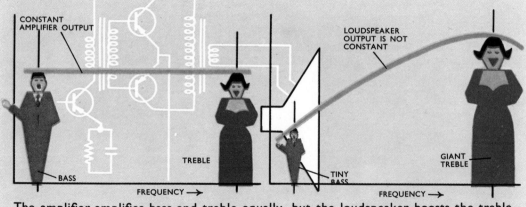

The amplifier amplifies bass and treble equally, but the loudspeaker boosts the treble.

Boosting the Bass

The transistors in the final stage amplify all signals fairly equally, over the audible range. So if two signals of the same volume corresponding to different notes, one of middle C, and the other the note an octave higher, arrive at the final stage, they will both be amplified by the same amount.

Unfortunately, the loudspeaker does not work in this way. It tends to accentuate the higher frequency signals. So even though the loudspeaker was given electrical impulses of the same size, the note an octave higher would come out of the loudspeaker louder than the middle C.

Of course, this means that the notes are not each at their proper volume, and the reproduction would not be very good. For this reason *feedback* components, a capacitor and a resistor, are included in the circuit. The electrical properties of the capacitor depend on the frequency of the signal, so it is able to allow back more high frequency signals than low frequency signals.

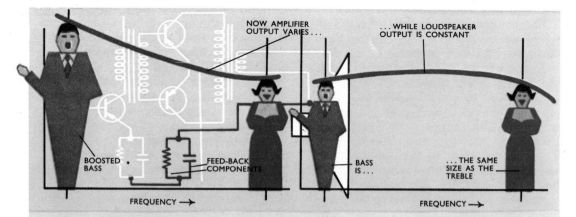

The feed-back capacitor allows back more treble than bass, and this has the effect of reducing the treble coming from the amplifier.

—G

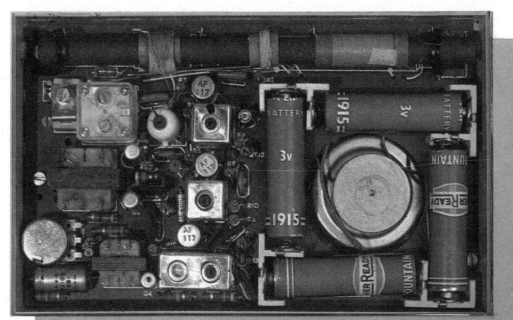

The completed transistor super-het receiver. The components are now soldered on to the printed circuit board. Four 1½ volt batteries, connected in series, supply power to the set. The ferrite-rod aerial goes along the top.

ALIGNING THE SUPER-HET

Aligning a radio set means making final adjustments to some of the components, to get the best performance out of it. Aligning involves expensive equipment—a signal generator, capable of producing electrical oscillations over the range 50 cycles per second to 1,600 kilocycles per second (1,600,000 cycles per second) and an output meter which measures the amount of power reaching the loudspeaker.

The procedure is fairly simple. The signal generator feeds a certain type of signal into various parts of the set, and the output meter measures what the transistor set does to the signal.

It is usual to work backwards, starting at the final stage, the audio-frequency amplifier. The output meter is always connected to the two loudspeaker terminals in place of the loudspeaker, and it measures the volume of signal being fed into the loudspeaker. The *frequency* response of the audio frequency amplifiers is to be tested first. In other words the maker of the set wants to know whether the output meter gives the same sort of reading for a signal of 300 cycles per second as it

does for a signal of frequency 3,000 cycles per second. This frequency range covers the range of sound waves likely to be given out by the small loudspeaker of a portable transistor set.

The signal generator provides the necessary signal. This is a 'pure' signal, of one frequency only. To make sure that the set itself does not complicate this signal during this operation, the frequency selection knob is twisted so that no signals are being picked up. The signal generator is connected across the two terminals of the volume control resistor. Various frequencies over the audible range are fed in, and the corresponding meter readings noted down.

Because the loudspeaker tends to boost the higher frequencies, components are inserted into the set to boost the lower frequencies (the 'bass'). As a result, the output meter should give a higher reading for 300 cycles per second than for 3,000 cycles per second. The exact amount by which one is greater than the other can be worked out only if the characteristics of the loudspeaker are known. The only possible adjustments are in the feedback resistors which are 'boosting the bass'.

The components which will most probably need aligning are the transformers in the intermediate frequency stage. They are part of tuned circuits, and they must be tuned to the *intermediate frequency* (the result of the *heterodyning*), which in this set is about 465 kilocycles per second. These transformers are provided with an iron dust core (it increases their inductance), which can be screwed in and out. In this way their inductance, and the frequency to which the circuit is tuned, is altered.

It is important to note that the transformer cores must not be screwed in with iron or steel screwdrivers, for these are *ferromagnetic* and would add to the effective inductance of the transformer, giving a false value to the tuned frequency. A non-ferrous tool (e.g. made of copper) must be used instead.

The procedure is to feed a small signal of frequency 465 kilocycles per second modulated with a 'pure' audio frequency signal into the set via a 'blocking capacitor' and to adjust the transformers, one at a time, so that the output is maximum (measured by the output meter). The modulation is necessary because the 465 kilocycle per second

signal is disposed of before it reaches the output meter. Only where it carries an audible frequency can the signal give a reading on the output meter.

The signal is fed into the set (see diagram), and a signal of up to half a volt is needed to give a reading on the output meter. But as the transformers are aligned more closely, the output from the signal generator must be lowered. The last transformer is adjusted first, then the middle one, and finally the first transformer. The transformers are adjusted simply by screwing in or out the iron-dust cores. During this operation, the receiver is switched to the medium waveband.

The next step is to align the first stage, which receives the radio-frequency signal. When this is done, the signal generator is not connected directly to the set. Instead it is used as a transmitting station, a few coils of wire connected across its output terminals acting as a transmitting aerial. First the signal generator transmits a signal of frequency 525 kilocycles per second. This represents the lowest frequency of the medium waveband. The transistor set is switched on to the medium waveband,

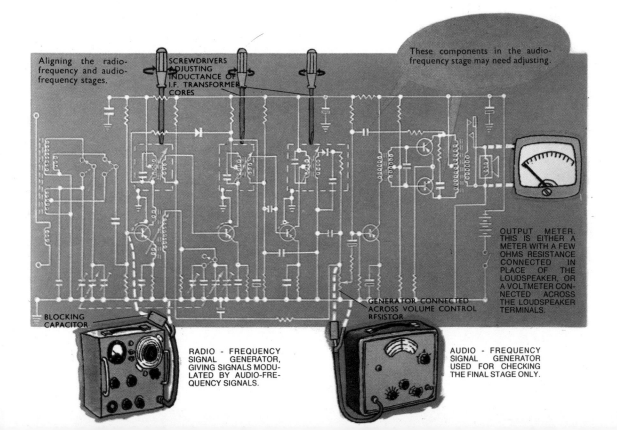

Aligning the radio-frequency and audio-frequency stages.

SCREWDRIVERS ADJUSTING INDUCTANCE OF I.F. TRANSFORMER CORES

These components in the audio-frequency stage may need adjusting.

OUTPUT METER. THIS IS EITHER A METER WITH A FEW OHMS RESISTANCE CONNECTED IN PLACE OF THE LOUDSPEAKER, OR A VOLTMETER CONNECTED ACROSS THE LOUDSPEAKER TERMINALS.

GENERATOR CONNECTED ACROSS VOLUME CONTROL RESISTOR

BLOCKING CAPACITOR

RADIO - FREQUENCY SIGNAL GENERATOR, GIVING SIGNALS MODULATED BY AUDIO-FREQUENCY SIGNALS.

AUDIO - FREQUENCY SIGNAL GENERATOR USED FOR CHECKING THE FINAL STAGE ONLY.

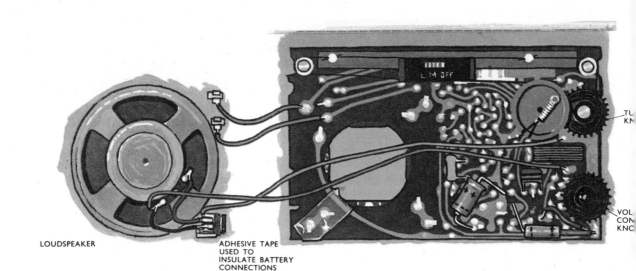

LOUDSPEAKER

ADHESIVE TAPE
USED TO
INSULATE BATTERY
CONNECTIONS

and the frequency selector knob twisted so that it is right off the lower frequency (longest wavelength) end of the scale. Then the iron dust core of the oscillator transformer is screwed either in or out until the output is a maximum on the output meter.

The generator is readjusted so that it transmits a 1,600 kilocycle signal. This represents the upper limit of the medium waveband, and the frequency control knob is twisted right to the other end of the scale. The 'trimming' capacitor

attached to the oscillator might have to be adjusted now to give a maximum output.

Aerial coils and 'trimming' capacitors attached to the aerial are adjusted (again for maximum output on the output meter) while the set is receiving the signal generator's signals at various points along the medium waveband.

A similar procedure is followed for the long waveband, the components which need adjusting at each stage depending ultimately on the design of the set.

To align the radio-frequency stage, the signal generator is used as a transmitter. Different radio-frequencies (modulated with audio-frequencies) are transmitted. The set is tuned to receive them.

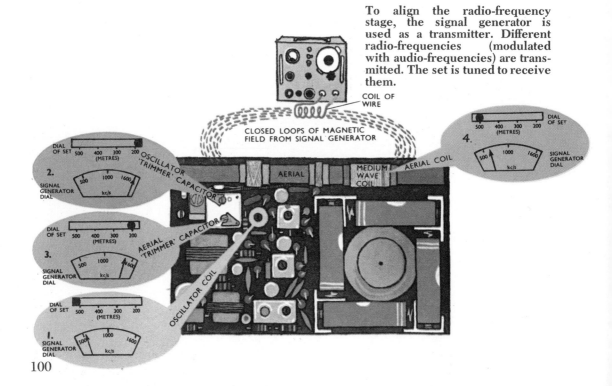

COMPONENTS IN THE TRANSISTOR CIRCUITS

The circuit diagrams shown on previous pages have been designed to illustrate the principles involved in the operation of the various stages in the superhet receiver. They are not intended to be used in the construction of a working model and the component values listed below for the various circuits are given as examples of typical components that might be used:

Heterodyning the signal (page 86)

$C_5 = 0·1\mu F$
C_2 is a tuning capacitor
$C_1 = 0·1\mu F$
$R_1 = 33K\Omega$
$R_2 = 6·8K\Omega$
$C_3 = 0·01\mu F$
$R_3 = 560K\Omega$
$R_4 = 150K\Omega$
C_4 is a tuning capacitor

The I.F. Amplifiers (page 90)

$C_6 = 144pF$
$C_5 = 0·1\mu F$
$R_5 = 100\Omega$
$R_6 = 33K\Omega$
$C_7 = 10\mu F$
$R_7 = 8·2K\Omega$
$C_8 = 0·1\mu F$
$R_8 = 470\Omega$
$R_9 = 18K\Omega$
$R_{10} = 3·3K\Omega$
$C_{10} = 0·047\mu F$
$R_{11} = 470\Omega$
$C_{11} = 0·047\mu F$
$C_9 = 250pF$
$C_{12} = 250pF$

The Audio Frequency Amplifier (page 96)

$R_{16} = 15K\Omega$
$C_{15} = 5pF$
$R_{15} = 3·9K\Omega$
$R_{18} = 2·7K\Omega$
$R_{19} = 58\Omega$
$R_{20} = 4·7\Omega$

Detecting the signal (page 92)

$C_6 = 250pF$
$R_6 = 33\Omega$
$C_7 = 10\mu F$
$C_8 = 0·1\mu F$
$R_8 = 470\Omega$
$C_9 = 250pF$
$R_9 = 18K\Omega$
$R_{10} = 18K\Omega$
$C_{10} = 0·04\mu F$
$R_{11} = 470\Omega$
$C_{11} = 0·047pF$
$C_{12} = 250pF$
$R_{13} = 330\Omega$
$C_{13} = 0·047\mu F$
$C_{14} = 0·047\mu F$

$$1pF = 1 \text{ pica Farad} = \frac{1}{1,000.000.000.000} \text{ Farad}$$

VALVES AND TRANSISTORS COMPARED

Both valves and transistors control the flow of currents through electronic circuits. They are used to amplify currents, detect electrical signals, change steady currents into oscillating currents, or to act as switches, turning currents on and off. They have a growing number of other applications.

An electric current is a flow of electrons. In a valve, the current is controlled as it jumps across a vacuum (or sometimes through gas) from one piece of conducting metal (the cathode) to another piece (the anode). The transistor, however, is all solid. The current passes through slices of *semiconducting material*—germanium or silicon made specially conductive by adding impurities to them.

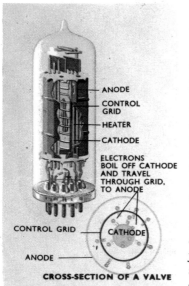

CROSS-SECTION OF A VALVE

ANODE
CONTROL GRID
HEATER
CATHODE
ELECTRONS BOIL OFF CATHODE AND TRAVEL THROUGH GRID, TO ANODE

CONTROL GRID
CATHODE
ANODE

In a vacuum triode valve, a cloud of electrons is boiled away from the heated cathode. It is controlled by the electrode in between cathode and anode, the grid.

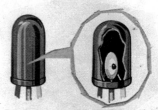

The transistor is made from solid, semiconducting material. The inset shows the actual transistor, normally hidden inside the case.

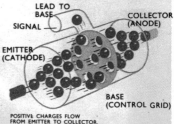

LEAD TO BASE
SIGNAL
COLLECTOR (ANODE)
EMITTER (CATHODE)
BASE (CONTROL GRID)

POSITIVE CHARGES FLOW FROM EMITTER TO COLLECTOR. THIS IS EQUIVALENT TO ELECTRON FLOW CURRENT (NEGATIVE CHARGES) IN THE OPPOSITE DIRECTION

The cathode, grid and anode of the triode valve correspond to the emitter, base and collector of the transistor. The flow of current is normally controlled through the base.

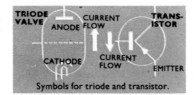

TRIODE VALVE
ANODE
CURRENT FLOW
TRANS-ISTOR
CATHODE
CURRENT FLOW
EMITTER

Symbols for triode and transistor.

POSITIVE BATTERY TERMINAL +
RESISTOR
CAPACITOR
ANODE
GRID
OUTPUT BETWEEN CATHODE AND ANODE
CATHODE
HEATER
INPUT SIGNAL
NEGATIVE BATTERY TERMINAL −

Circuit diagram for a typical triode amplifier. This valve is a *voltage* amplifier.

Normally the grid is kept more negative than the cathode, so that it repels electrons back to the cathode. If the signal voltage makes the cathode less negative, the current increases. But then the voltage difference between anode and cathode drops by a comparatively large amount.

Transistors amplify currents rather than voltages. The signal currents enters via the base. It, in effect, 'plugs' the gaps in the base, and causes a much bigger change in the current flowing from emitter to collector in the transistor.

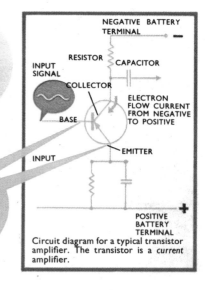

NEGATIVE BATTERY TERMINAL −
RESISTOR
CAPACITOR
INPUT SIGNAL
COLLECTOR
ELECTRON FLOW CURRENT FROM NEGATIVE TO POSITIVE
BASE
EMITTER
INPUT
POSITIVE BATTERY TERMINAL +

Circuit diagram for a typical transistor amplifier. The transistor is a *current* amplifier.

PART THREE

The Cathode Ray
Oscilloscope

The Cathode Ray Oscilloscope

THE CATHODE RAY OSCILLOSCOPE

AT FIRST sight the cathode-ray oscilloscope (or oscillograph) looks like a small television set with a bewilderingly large collection of knobs. In fact, the oscilloscope is similar to a television set in

It is possible to move, or deflect, the electron beam, and to make it follow the movement of the wave pattern of any electric current. The pin-point of light traces out a path (called a *trace*) on the screen. The oscilloscope pictures the movement of the electric current.

A simplified side-view of the Cathode Ray Tube

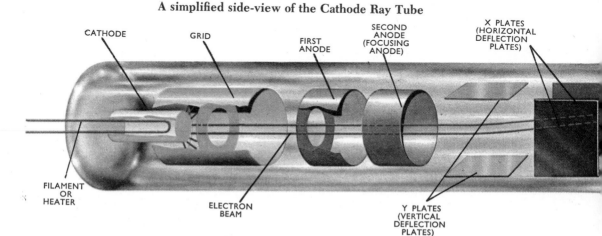

CATHODE   GRID   FIRST ANODE   SECOND ANODE (FOCUSING ANODE)   X PLATES (HORIZONTAL DEFLECTION PLATES)

FILAMENT OR HEATER   ELECTRON BEAM   Y PLATES (VERTICAL DEFLECTION PLATES)

many ways; and though the number of knobs is large, each performs a very simple function. A beam of electrons is produced in a tube, which is just like a television tube, and similar to the tubes of electronic valves. The beam strikes a fluorescent (light-emitting) screen, where it appears as a pin-point of light.

The beam is moved by devices called *plates* (which are actually capacitor plates). There are two sets of these — the *X-plates*, which deflect the beam horizontally, and the *Y-plates*, which deflect it vertically. On the front of most oscilloscopes are two terminals, which are usually called 'X' and 'Y'. Suppose an

How the Grid works

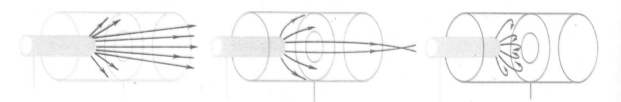

(Left): When there is no difference between the cathode voltage and the grid voltage, electrons streaming from the cathode pass unhindered through the hole in the grid. (Centre): If a voltage is arranged to make the grid more negative than the cathode, the grid repels electrons. Only the fast moving ones can get through. (Right): If the voltage makes the grid much more negative than the cathode none of the electrons can get through, so the beam is stopped.

ordinary battery is connected across the 'Y' and the 'earth' terminals. This gives a steady voltage, and it moves the pin-point of light either up or down, depending on which way round the battery has been connected. A similar, but horizontal,

A TELEVISION set would be useless without a screen to show the picture. This is the front part of the cathode ray tube. The tube is a cylinder of glass

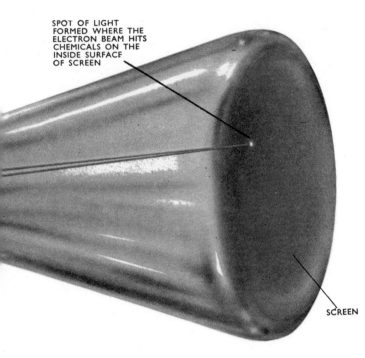

SPOT OF LIGHT FORMED WHERE THE ELECTRON BEAM HITS CHEMICALS ON THE INSIDE SURFACE OF SCREEN

SCREEN

deflection occurs when the battery is connected across the 'X' and the 'earth' terminals. There are two other knobs, which are called X-shift and Y-shift, and which do precisely the same thing as the battery by a convenient switching in of a D.C. voltage. With these knobs the spot of light can be moved, by a succession of horizontal and vertical steps, all over the screen. X-shift and Y-shift are sometimes marked, or *calibrated* in voltages. This is because the larger the voltage applied to the plates, the greater the deflection on the screen.

about five centimetres in diameter which widens out at one end and in the largest tubes which are used in television sets can have its face up to sixty centimetres across. The remarkable thing which a cathode ray tube can do is to turn an invisible movement of electrons, providing it is a repeated movement, into *something which can be seen* at the wide end of the tube.

The first important part of the tube is the *cathode* which, as in all electronic tubes, produces a stream of electrons when it is heated. These electrons pass straightaway through a *grid,* so called because it acts like the grid in a triode valve. However the cathode ray tube 'grid' is usually made in the form of a

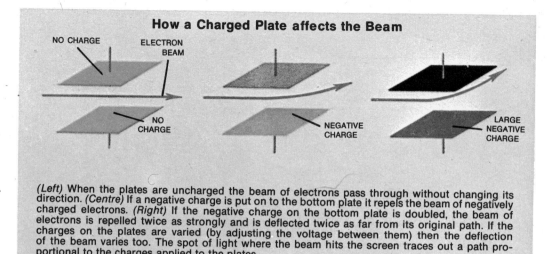

How a Charged Plate affects the Beam

NO CHARGE

ELECTRON BEAM

NO CHARGE

NEGATIVE CHARGE

LARGE NEGATIVE CHARGE

(Left) When the plates are uncharged the beam of electrons pass through without changing its direction. *(Centre)* If a negative charge is put on to the bottom plate it repels the beam of negatively charged electrons. *(Right)* If the negative charge on the bottom plate is doubled, the beam of electrons is repelled twice as strongly and is deflected twice as far from its original path. If the charges on the plates are varied (by adjusting the voltage between them) then the deflection of the beam varies too. The spot of light where the beam hits the screen traces out a path proportional to the charges applied to the plates.

circular disc inside a cylinder so that the beam passes through it in one single 'strand' and is not split into many smaller strands as it would be if the usual wire grid were used. The purpose of the grid in the cathode ray tube is to limit the number of electrons which make up the beam and so control the number which get to the screen. This in turn controls the brightness of the trace on the screen.

Several stages are involved in making and deflecting the electron beam. These will be described in more detail in the following chapters.

Next the electrons pass through a pair of cylinders which have a very large positive electrical charge on them. These are called the *anode* since anode is the name given to the final electrode which follows the grid in usual electronic valves. This is not a very good name in this case, however, since the anode in the cathode ray tube does not collect electrons as does the one in the usual valve; in fact its purpose is to make the electrons travel faster down the tube. The anode also has the important property of making the electrons bunch together into a narrow beam so that they appear as a fine spot and not as a blur on the face of the tube.

Now that the beam has been speeded up and made very narrow, the effects of an electric voltage can be applied to it. This can be done using a pair of *deflector plates*—small metal plates held one on

either side of the beam. If a voltage is applied to the plates so that they become charged, the beam will be deflected when it passes between them. The amount which the beam is deflected is proportional to the voltage applied to the plates. The deflected beam then carries on to hit the face of the tube at some point.

One pair of plates can cause the beam to move either towards or away from one of the plates; it cannot make it move in the other direction (which in the diagram is in or out of the paper). In order to cause this movement in a second direction a second pair of plates is put into the tube so that they are at right angles to the first pair. This second vertical pair of plates used alone can make the beam move in and out of the paper but not up and down. However, with both pairs of plates used together the direction of the beam can be altered in order to make it reach any point on the face of the screen.

The point on the face where the electron beam hits it is made visible by coating the inside of the face of the tube with a fluorescent material (usually zinc sulphide) which gives out a bright green light when electrons fall upon it. Then, if the voltage of the vertical plates is changed, the spot moves across the tube in what would be the X-direction on a graph. For this reason the vertical plates are called the *X-plates*. Similarly, if the voltage of the horizontal plates is changed

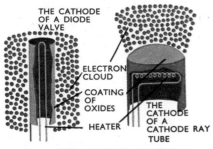

THE CATHODE OF A DIODE VALVE

ELECTRON CLOUD

COATING OF OXIDES

HEATER

THE CATHODE OF A CATHODE RAY TUBE

THE ELECTRON BEAM
How the cathode produces the electron beam

It has already been shown that electrons can be produced (for use in a diode or triode valve) by heating a metal tube which has been coated with a mixture of strontium and barium oxides. The electrons escape from the surface of the oxides.

The long tube produces a 'cloud' of electrons which spreads out towards the anode. In the cathode ray tube a *beam* of electrons is required so the mixture of oxides is coated onto the end of a 'cap' as shown. And instead of one anode surrounding the cathode, the cathode ray tube has at least two anodes placed in line with the cathode.

Why should the strange mixture of strontium and barium oxides be used for coating the cathode? All metals and many other substances will give off electrons if they are heated strongly enough. However, different substances have to be heated by different amounts; the substance which is chosen is the one which will produce the largest number of electrons with the smallest amount of heating (since the heat has to be produced using electric current which has to be paid for). The most efficient substance is found to be the mixture of oxides which is used.

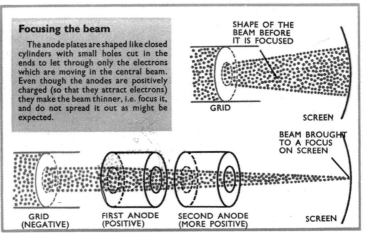

Focusing the beam

The anode plates are shaped like closed cylinders with small holes cut in the ends to let through only the electrons which are moving in the central beam. Even though the anodes are positively charged (so that they attract electrons) they make the beam thinner, i.e. focus it, and do not spread it out as might be expected.

SHAPE OF THE BEAM BEFORE IT IS FOCUSED

GRID

SCREEN

BEAM BROUGHT TO A FOCUS ON SCREEN

GRID (NEGATIVE)

FIRST ANODE (POSITIVE)

SECOND ANODE (MORE POSITIVE)

SCREEN

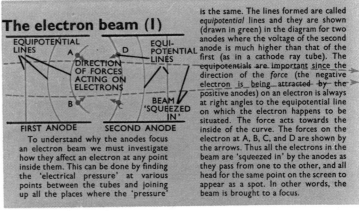

The electron beam (1)

EQUIPOTENTIAL LINES

EQUIPOTENTIAL LINES

DIRECTION OF FORCES ACTING ON ELECTRONS

BEAM 'SQUEEZED IN'

FIRST ANODE

SECOND ANODE

To understand why the anodes focus an electron beam we must investigate how they affect an electron at any point inside them. This can be done by finding the 'electrical pressure' at various points between the tubes and joining up all the places where the 'pressure' is the same. The lines formed are called *equipotential* lines and they are shown (drawn in green) in the diagram for two anodes where the voltage of the second anode is much higher than that of the first (as in a cathode ray tube). The equipotentials are important since the direction of the *force* (the negative electron is being attracted by the positive anodes) on an electron is always at right angles to the equipotential line on which the electron happens to be situated. The force acts towards the inside of the curve. The forces on the electron at A, B, C, and D are shown by the arrows. Thus all the electrons in the beam are 'squeezed in' by the anodes as they pass from one to the other, and all head for the same point on the screen to appear as a spot. In other words, the beam is brought to a focus.

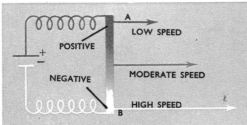

POSITIVE

A

LOW SPEED

NEGATIVE

MODERATE SPEED

HIGH SPEED

B

The electron beam (2)

The cathode in a valve or cathode ray tube is almost always indirectly heated, i.e. the heater is not directly connected to the cathode. If a voltage were applied to the cathode directly in order to produce the current to heat it, then one side of the plate (A) would be at a higher electrical pressure than the other side (B). Now electrons move from the cathode attracted by the anode which is positive, and the speed with which they move depends on the voltage between the point where they leave the cathode and the anode. Hence the electrons from one side of the cathode will move more quickly than electrons from the other. In the cathode ray tube this means that the spot will be brighter on one side than the other, and this is not a good thing. The difficulty is overcome by arranging a separate heater close behind the cathode. Then the cathode will be heated by radiation (see page 12) while it remains at the same electrical pressure over the whole of its surface and the electrons will all be accelerated by the same amount.

By the time they reach the anode in the cathode ray tube the electrons are moving so fast that they pass through the hole in the middle instead of moving out and coming to rest on the anode as electrons do in valves.

107

What a Time Base does

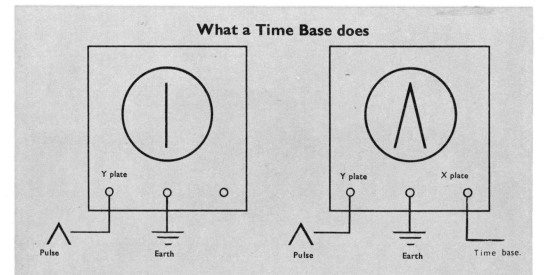

If a pulse which rises and falls again as shown is applied to one Y-plate of the oscilloscope (the other being earthed) then, since the Y-plate can only make the spot move in the vertical direction, a vertical line will appear on the face of the screen. However, if the spot is drawn to the side at the same time as the pulse reaches the plate then the height of the pulse at different times will be spread out across the screen so that a 'picture' of the pulse is produced. If the pulse takes more than about 1/20th of a second to rise and then fall we shall see the spot rise and fall again as it moves across the screen. However, pulses occurring thousands or even, in specially designed oscilloscopes, many millions of times in each second can be looked at on the screen. This is done by making the spot fly *back* to its starting position at the end of each pulse to follow the next one across the screen and so on. If each pulse is exactly the same then the spot will move over exactly the same path on the face of the cathode ray tube each time and we shall only be able to see a steady trace. The dot will follow the shape of the pulse, however complicated.

A picture of the pulse required from the Time Base

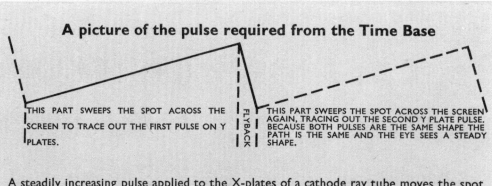

THIS PART SWEEPS THE SPOT ACROSS THE SCREEN TO TRACE OUT THE FIRST PULSE ON Y PLATES.

FLYBACK

THIS PART SWEEPS THE SPOT ACROSS THE SCREEN AGAIN, TRACING OUT THE SECOND Y PLATE PULSE. BECAUSE BOTH PULSES ARE THE SAME SHAPE THE PATH IS THE SAME AND THE EYE SEES A STEADY SHAPE.

A steadily increasing pulse applied to the X-plates of a cathode ray tube moves the spot across the screen. When the spot reaches the other side the pulse must quickly fall again so that the spot can move rapidly back to the other side of the screen for the start of the next pulse applied to the Y-plates. For a continuous series of pulses applied to the Y-plates a continuous series of pulses must be applied to the X-plates so the pulses from the time base must be repeated as shown by the dotted line.

the spot moves vertically on the screen, i.e. in the Y-direction, so these are called the *Y-plates*. Electrons are very light and small compared with the gas molecules which are in the air and if an electron hits one of these molecules it will be stopped or its direction changed. To prevent this from happening to the electron beam as much of the air as possible is pumped out of the tube during manufacture.

The distance that the spot moves on the face of the tube can be used to measure the voltage applied to the plates. The sensitivity of the oscilloscope is given by the manufacturers and is the number of volts needed to move the beam, say, one inch. Most oscilloscopes have a number of different sensitivities, which range from perhaps 100 volts/inch to 100 millivolts/inch (a millivolt is a thousandth of a volt). If the voltage being examined is about 1 volt, then the instrument is switched on to the 1 volt/inch range. The most important use, however, of the cathode ray tube is to show a repeated voltage, however complicated, as a pattern on the tube face. What is more, a pattern can be produced even when the voltage is repeated many *million* times each second. With an oscilloscope the voltage can be measured at

any time during the repeated change (usually called a *cycle*) and also the time which the cycle takes from start to finish. In order to use the cathode ray tube in a television set a very complicated series of voltage pulses has to be applied to the deflection plates to make the spot produce a picture on the screen.

THE TIME BASE

It has already been mentioned that if a series of electrical pulses reach the 'Y-plates' of a cathode ray tube then the spot on the screen of the tube will move up and down in time with the pulses. If the movement of the spot is quick enough then a vertical line will be seen on the screen since the movement of the spot itself will be too quick for the eye to follow. From the length of this line the maximum voltage of the pulse can be measured but the line gives no information about the pulse when it is not at its greatest value. To learn more about this, it is necessary to draw the spot out across the screen in time with the pulse. This is done using an electronic device called a *time base* — it allows us to see the size of the pulse at any time.

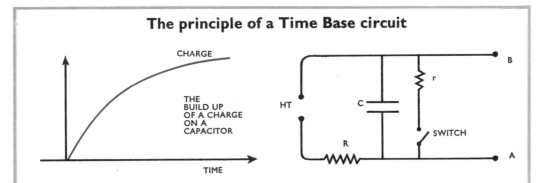

The principle of a Time Base circuit

CHARGE

THE BUILD UP OF A CHARGE ON A CAPACITOR

TIME

HT

C

r

B

SWITCH

R

A

When the circuit is connected to the H.T. terminals electrons flow through the resistor R to charge the capacitor C. Hence the electrical 'pressure' of the point A gradually rises. When the 'pressure' difference or voltage between points A and B reaches a certain value the switch is closed and the capacitor will discharge itself quickly through the small resistor r so that the voltage between points A and B will fall back to zero. If the switch is then broken the capacitor then starts to charge again so the cycle is repeated. The pulse at AB is similar to the one that we required for the time base.

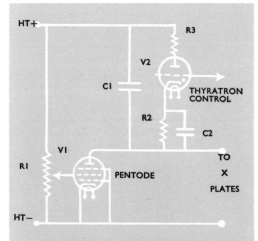

Symbol
for a
THYRATRON

HT POSITIVE

TIME BASE CAPACITOR C1

R3

THYRATRON
CONTROL

FINE CONTROL
OF FREQUENCY OF
TIME BASE PULSES
GIVEN BY VARIABLE
RESISTOR
R1   SCREEN
GRID

THYRATRON
V2

V1
GAS-FILLED
THYRATRON

C2

SUPPRESSOR
EARTHING
LEAD

GRID EARTHING
LEAD

R2

TO
X
PLATES

HT
NEGATIVE   CATHODE
LEAD

FILAMENT
LEADS

**The circuit model for the time base circuit.
The corresponding diagram is shown below.**

HT+

R3

V2

C1   THYRATRON
CONTROL

R2

C2

V1

R1   TO

PENTODE   X

PLATES

HT−

THE TIME BASE CIRCUIT

C_1 is the time base capacitor. R_1 is a
variable resistor which gives a very fine
control over the frequency of the time
base pulses. R_2 and C_2 ensure that the
cathode of the thyratron is at the correct
voltage. Resistor R_3 is inserted between
the anode and the high tension positive
supply so that when the valve conducts
the current does not become large
enough to damage it.

In order to change the up-and-down
movement of the spot into a picture of
the pulse applied to the plates, the time
base needs to make the spot *sweep*
smoothly across the screen and then *fly
back* to the left-hand side to start on the
next pulse which arrives. This can be
arranged by applying a steadily increasing charge to the 'X-plates' (to draw the
spot across) and then to remove the
charge quickly when the spot has
reached the other side of the screen so
that it returns to its original position.

This can be done by charging a
capacitor gradually (through a resistor)
so that the voltage across its plates
increases and then arranging a switch
to discharge it when the voltage across
the capacitor reaches the required
value (i.e. when the spot reaches the
other side of the screen). The first
part of the increase is almost exactly
proportional to time, i.e. gets larger by
equal amounts after equal lengths of
time. This is just what is required from
a time base.

The first type of time base which was
used with cathode ray tubes had a *thyratron* valve acting as the discharging
switch. This valve is a triode valve consisting of a cathode, grid and anode held
in a glass tube. But unlike an ordinary

triode where all the gas is pumped out of the tube before it is sealed, a small amount of mercury is introduced into the thyratron. This is in the form of a vapour, since the pressure in the tube is still very low. The mercury atoms become charged, i.e. *ionized,* when electrons collide with them. The ionized vapour is a good conductor so very much larger currents can be passed through a thyratron than through an ordinary vacuum tube. However, the mercury will only conduct when it is ionized. The ionization is started by fast moving electrons hitting mercury atoms sufficiently hard to knock further electrons out of them. Since the negative bias on the grid slows down the flow of electrons from cathode to anode, the *start* of ionization is controlled by the grid-bias voltage. If the thyratron is connected in *parallel* with

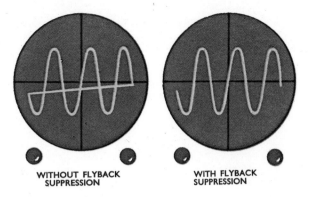

WITHOUT FLYBACK SUPPRESSION WITH FLYBACK SUPPRESSION

the capacitor so that the voltage across each is the same, the capacitor will charge up slowly until the voltage across it and across the valve reaches some particular value (determined by the grid-bias). Then the mercury vapour will suddenly ionize and provide an easy path short-circuiting the capacitor. The

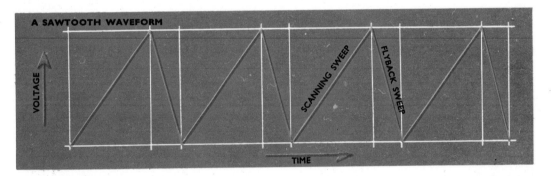

A SAWTOOTH WAVEFORM

VOLTAGE

SCANNING SWEEP

FLYBACK SWEEP

TIME

Below: The flyback quenching circuit is shown in yellow. It consists of a capacitor and a diode valve and has the effect of converting the very short pulse of electrons which appears at the anode of the thyratron when it conducts (i.e. during flyback) into a negative pulse which can be applied to the grid of the cathode ray tube to suppress the electron beam.

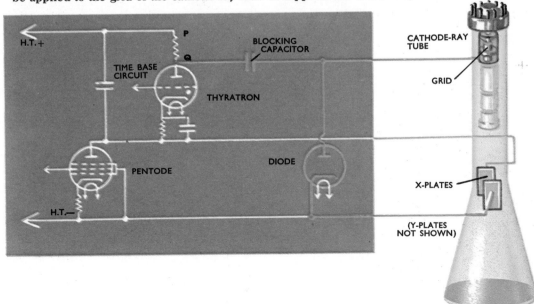

charges stored on the plates of the capacitor therefore escape rapidly through the thyratron. When the capacitor has discharged there is no voltage across it or across the thyratron which therefore ceases to conduct. The process starts all over again.

The cathode of the thyratron and the side of the capacitor connected to it are wired to one of the oscilloscope's X-plates. The other X-plate is 'earthed' to the chassis. Hence the voltage applied to the X-plates (which deflect the spot horizontally across the screen) varies with the charge on the capacitor.

To ensure that the capacitor charges up at an even rate a pentode valve is connected into the circuit instead of an ordinary resistor.

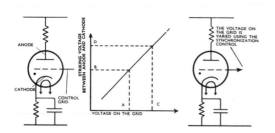

How the pulse to be examined is itself used to trigger off the thyratron valve in the timebase and hence to start the spot of light sweeping across the screen.

A thyratron valve will not conduct electricity until the voltage between its anode and cathode reaches some particular value (whereupon the gas in the thyratron becomes ionized). This value is changed if the grid voltage is changed as shown in the graph. If the grid voltage is given by A, then, following the dotted lines, the graph shows that the thyratron will conduct when the voltage between its ends is given by B. If the voltage on the grid is made larger, corresponding to C, say, then a larger voltage D can be applied between the plates before the thyratron will conduct.

This property of the thyratron can be used to make the moment when it conducts (which governs the repetition rate) coincide with the moment when the pulse is to be displayed is at its most positive, simply by leading a small amount of the pulse directly to the grid. The thyratron will then always conduct when the pulse is most positive so the moment of flyback (which occurs when the thyratron conducts) will now always come *at the same time as the maximum of the pulse.* It is still necessary to vary the frequency of the timebase since, if the repetition rate of the timebase is very different from the frequency of the pulse, the effect of the grid will not be big enough to make the repetition rate and the pulse frequency *synchronize.*

To see different parts of the series of pulses.

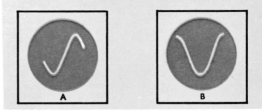

When the pentode is connected as shown on page 110 it allows only a constant current to pass regardless of the difference in potential between the anode and the grid. The middle grid controls the current flowing through (as the single grid does in a triode valve) while the grids on either side of it prevent any charges on the anode or the cathode from affecting the middle one. Hence the valve passes the same current (i.e. allows electrons through at the same rate) regardless of the charge on the anode plate. In this way a capacitor can be made to charge up at an even rate.

SUPPRESSING THE FLYBACK TRACE

The *timebase* of an oscilloscope is responsible for the left-to-right movement of the spot of light across the screen. It is simply a circuit whose output voltage rises steadily to a maximum and then drops steadily but more rapidly to its original value. A graph of the timebase voltage is called a *sawtooth* waveform for reasons which are obvious from the diagram. The frequency of the sawtooth voltage is adjusted until it coincides exactly with the frequency of the pulse (or the frequency of a number of pulses) being displayed. This 'synchronization', as it is called, ensures that the pattern on the screen remains stationary. If a sawtooth voltage is applied to the X-plates of an oscilloscope the spot of light moves forwards and backwards across the screen. The rapid right-to-left, or backward, motion is known as the *flyback.* It is very desirable *not* to see the spot as

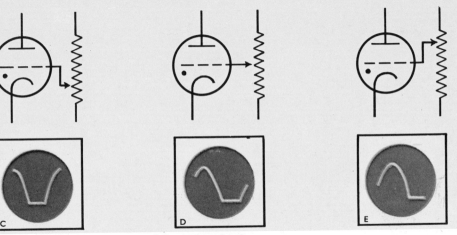

To see different parts of the series of pulses.

When examining a sine wave displayed on the oscilloscope screen it does not much matter which parts of the pulse are visible as long as a complete pulse appears on the screen. It can appear as on A or on B and yet there is no mistaking what curve it is.

However, for a more complicated curve (e.g. the one shown in C, D and E which comes from a half-wave rectifier) it may be better to select different parts of the wave. For example, the picture C would arise from the type of synchronisation so far described, but different parts of the wave may be selected (such as D and E).

The picture can be 'shifted' across the screen by making the timebase cause the flyback to occur at a different part of the pulse. This can be done very easily by arranging a resistor with a sliding contact connected to the grid of the thyratron as shown in the small circuit diagram. If the contact on the resistor is raised then the effect of the pulse on the grid is greater; now the pulse does not have to rise to its maximum before the thyratron will conduct. By moving the contact on the resistor up and down, the part of the pulse which makes the thyratron conduct can be varied, hence any section of the pulse can be shown on the screen.

it flies back across the screen between pulses, since its movement in the right-to-left direction is not related to the pulse being displayed on the screen. For this reason a *flyback quenching circuit* is employed to suppress the electron beam during the moment of flyback.

Suppression of the electron beam can be achieved by making the grid of the cathode ray tube more than usually negative—so negative in fact that the negatively charged electrons are repelled back from it and never reach the screen. But of course extra negative bias must be given to the grid only during the right-to-left movement of the spot or the pattern will disappear altogether. So the extra grid bias is obtained from some point in the time base circuit which is *negative during the flyback movement.*

The full circuit diagram for a *synchronized thyratron timebase* which can produce a wide range of repetition rates. It has both coarse and fine frequency controls.

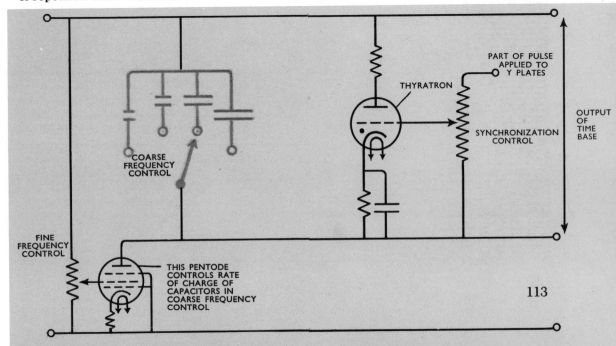

113

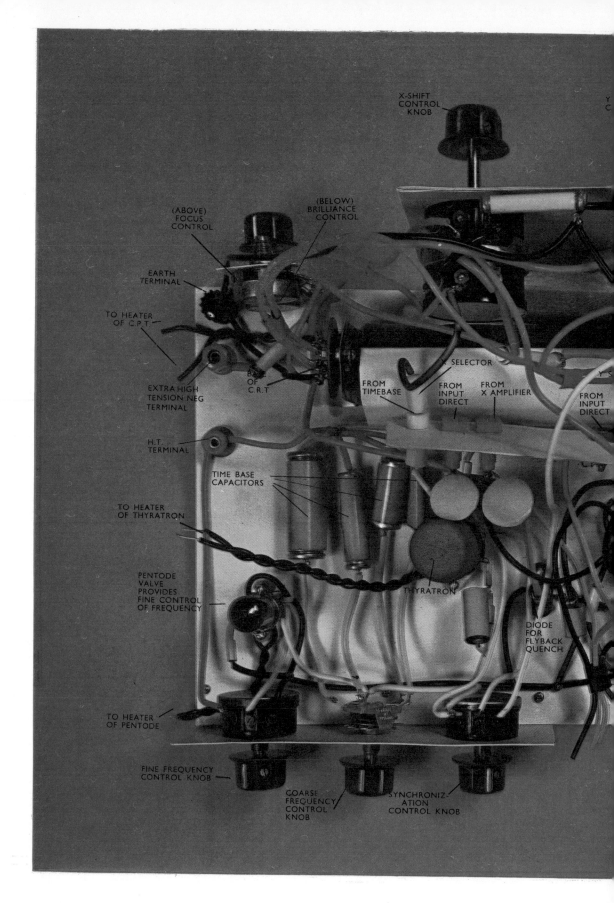

X-SHIFT
CONTROL
KNOB

Y S ... C ...

(ABOVE)
FOCUS
CONTROL

(BELOW)
BRILLIANCE
CONTROL

EARTH
TERMINAL

TO HEATER
OF C.P.T.

SELECTOR

FROM
TIMEBASE

FROM
INPUT
DIRECT

FROM
X AMPLIFIER

FROM
INPUT
DIRECT

EXTRA HIGH
TENSION NEG
TERMINAL

BA ...
OF
C.R.T

H.T.
TERMINAL

TIME BASE
CAPACITORS

TO HEATER
OF THYRATRON

PENTODE
VALVE
PROVIDES
FINE CONTROL
OF FREQUENCY

THYRATRON

DIODE
FOR
FLYBACK
QUENCH

TO HEATER
OF PENTODE

FINE FREQUENCY
CONTROL KNOB

COARSE
FREQUENCY
CONTROL
KNOB

SYNCHRONIZ-
ATION
CONTROL KNOB

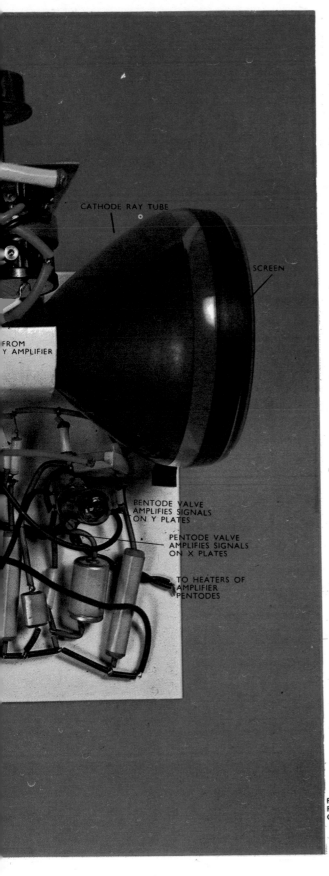

CATHODE RAY TUBE

SCREEN

FROM
Y AMPLIFIER

PENTODE VALVE
AMPLIFIES SIGNALS
ON Y PLATES

PENTODE VALVE
AMPLIFIES SIGNALS
ON X PLATES

TO HEATERS OF
AMPLIFIER
PENTODES

The full circuit of a simple cathode ray oscilloscope. This shows how the time-base, synchronization control, flyback quench and the amplifiers and direct lines to the X and Y plates are connected. Using a selector switch one side of the X plates can be connected either to the time-base or to the direct X line or the X amplifier. The other X plate is connected to a constant voltage. Hence it always has an opposite charge on it to the left-hand plate. The flyback quench is connected to the grid to make it very negative during the flyback period to stop the beam. The synchronization control is connected to the Y plate. One Y plate needs to be connected either directly to voltage pulses or to the Y amplifier. This is done by changing the two-way selector switch.

It is advisable to show only *oscillations* of voltage (i.e. voltage changes which periodically return to their original value), and not steady voltages, either negative or positive. If a steady voltage as well as the oscillation were applied to the deflection plates then the steady part could easily drive the spot completely off the screen, preventing the oscillating part (which is usually of more interest) from being displayed. Hence the *blocking* capacitors shown are included in the circuit. Capacitors allow only *variations* in voltage to pass and prevent the spot from being permanently shifted off the screen. The capacitor which is shown connected to the X plate does the same job in keeping the plate earthed since, although the X plate is connected to the H.T. terminal, the voltage on the plate is zero; a steady high voltage cannot pass through the capacitor.

The time-base and amplifier valves all need power to operate them. This comes from the positive H.T. line which is kept at its high voltage by another power rectifier (or, more often, another part of the same one used to supply the very high voltage for the tube controls). It is essential if the valves are to work steadily that their anodes should be kept at a constant voltage. But the timebase and the amplifiers usually have pulses passed into them and these could be passed from one component to the other. This is avoided by providing a path for any pulses which have been passed on to the H.T. line so that they can reach the earth line in preference to the next part. This is done by inserting a capacitor between earth and part of the anode resistance. The separated components are then said to be *decoupled*.

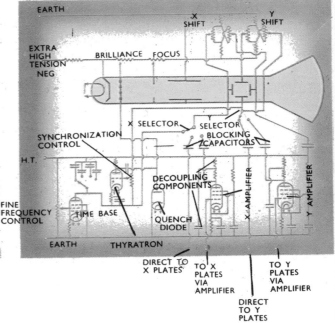

EARTH

X
SHIFT

Y
SHIFT

EXTRA
HIGH
TENSION
NEG

BRILLIANCE   FOCUS

X SELECTOR

SELECTOR

BLOCKING
CAPACITORS

SYNCHRONIZATION
CONTROL

H.T.

DECOUPLING
COMPONENTS

X AMPLIFIER

Y AMPLIFIER

FINE
FREQUENCY
CONTROL

TIME BASE

QUENCH
DIODE

EARTH   THYRATRON

DIRECT TO
X PLATES

TO X
PLATES
VIA
AMPLIFIER

TO Y
PLATES
VIA
AMPLIFIER

DIRECT
TO Y
PLATES

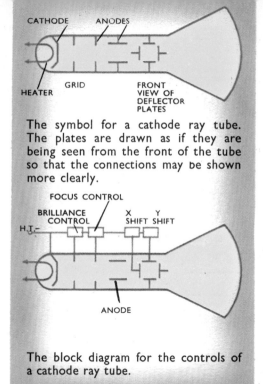

The symbol for a cathode ray tube. The plates are drawn as if they are being seen from the front of the tube so that the connections may be shown more clearly.

The block diagram for the controls of a cathode ray tube.

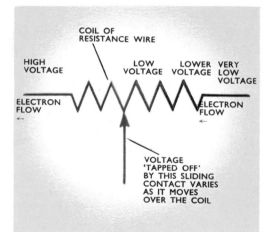

For the brilliance and focus controls a steady voltage is required which can be changed by hand when necessary. This can be obtained from a resistor with a current passed through it as shown. Then the voltage will change gradually along the resistor and, if a contact is arranged to slide along, then the voltage of the wire connected to the contact will vary. This is in fact done by turning one of the oscilloscope's knobs.

The point marked Q in the diagram on page 111 fulfils the required condition. This point lies between the anode of the thyratron and the resistor which protects the thyratron from excessively large surges of electrons when the timebase capacitor discharges during flyback. Electrons can only surge through the thyratron from cathode to anode and not in the reverse direction, so they have to pass through the resistor *from* the anode, not towards it (i.e. in the circuit diagram they pass upwards from Q to P). Since electrons flow from negative to positive, this means that point Q must be *negative during flyback*. Hence a lead from point Q to the grid of the cathode ray tube (via a capacitor to isolate the grid from the positive high tension supply) provides an easy means of suppressing the electron beam.

There is a drawback to this system in that point Q becomes positive while the time-base capacitor is charging up (i.e. during the left-to-right sweep). The positive charge at Q would make the grid of the cathode ray tube *less* than usually negative, with the result that more electrons would pass through the grid and the spot of light would become

Below: The full circuit diagram for the *tube controls* of a cathode ray oscilloscope. As always in a practical circuit, extra resistors (and sometimes capacitors) must be added to ensure that the components are working at the correct voltages and also that unwanted varying voltages are passed to the earth line (which is at zero voltage). For this reason, and in order to ensure that the X and Y shifts will move the spot just from one side of the screen to the other, the resistors shown here in orange are arranged on either side of the shifting device. The *high tension* (H.T.) voltage is obtained from a *power rectifier* (which is worked from the normal electric mains). In order to accelerate the electrons a very high voltage is needed. The voltage from the power rectifier may not be the best one for the working of the tube. For this reason the resistor shown in green is included in the circuit to reduce the voltage, making it the optimum value for the tube.

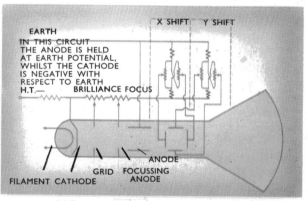

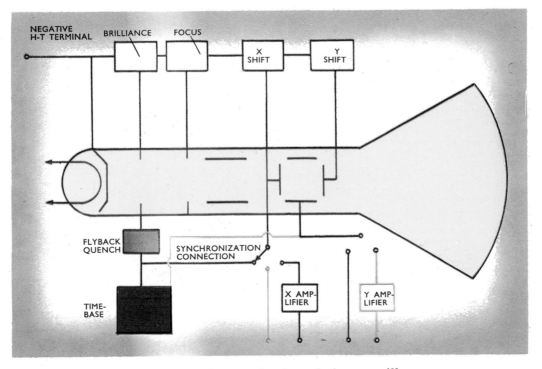

The full block diagram for the cathode ray oscilloscope.

The full block diagram for the cathode ray oscilloscope. The arrangements of the upper line of controls in the order BRILLIANCE, FOCUS, X SHIFT and Y SHIFT is far from haphazard. BRILLIANCE needs the highest negative voltage, so comes nearest the negative terminal. FOCUS needs the next highest negative voltage. Comparatively small negative voltages are needed to operate X SHIFT and Y SHIFT, so these come at the end of the line.

brighter. In order to ensure that the spot remains at the same brightness throughout the forward sweep, a *diode valve* is connected between the grid of the cathode ray tube and the negative high tension supply. The diode allows electrons (negative charges) to pass from cathode to anode and stops them passing from anode to cathode. With the anode of the diode connected to the grid of the cathode ray tube any tendency for the grid to become positive is immediately stopped since any positive charges on the grid are neutralized by electrons attracted through the diode. Thus the diode prevents the spot of light from brightening up during its passage across the screen.

SYNCHRONIZING THE OSCILLOSCOPE

The *timebase* can make the spot on the screen of a cathode-ray tube trace out the picture of a pulse which arrives at the Y plates, making the spot sweep across the screen while the pulse moves the spot up and down. Since the two movements take place at the same time the spot traces out a picture. In order to see just one complete cycle of the wave on the screen the spot must *fly back* every time a cycle is completed. This means that the frequency of the pulse from the time base must be *exactly* the same as the frequency of the pulse on the Y plates. Hence, if the oscilloscope needs to be used with pulses of more than one frequency (as is almost always the case) then the rate at which the capacitor in the time-base charges up, discharges and then begins to charge up again (called the *repetition rate*) must be adjustable.

One way of altering this rate is to vary the amount of current getting to the capacitor. If the current is increased the capacitor will charge up more quickly to reach the voltage at which the thyratron valve will discharge it. Hence the

117

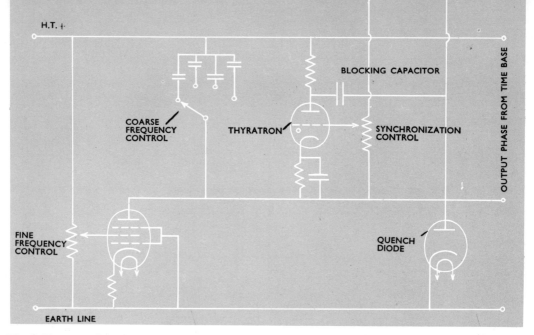

The full circuit diagram of the time base circuit. This is essentially a combination of the circuit diagrams on pages 111 and 113.

repetition rate is increased. The current supplied to the capacitor is increased by allowing more current through the pentode valve (not to be confused with the thyratron). This can be done by making the voltage on its grid less negative, simply by sliding the contact on the resistor connected to the grid upwards (i.e. upwards on the circuit diagram, but in practice this means turning a knob like the volume control on a radio set). Similarly, to reduce the repetition rate, the grid must be made more negative by sliding the contact on the resistor downwards. There is a limit, however, to the amount of current which can be passed through the valve without damaging it. Hence the frequency cannot be altered greatly by varying the grid voltage.

Fortunately another thing which does control the rate of charging of the capacitor (and, so, the repetition rate) is the size of the capacitor itself. Hence the repetition rate can be varied by changing the capacitor. This is done by arranging a number of capacitors, ranging from very small to quite large ones, in the circuit as shown. Then, by the movement of a switch, any one of the capacitors can be brought into the circuit. Using this method the repetition rate cannot be varied *smoothly* but only

by fixed amounts. For this reason *both* methods are used in oscilloscopes. This allows the repetition rate to be varied gradually over a very wide range.

Having a picture of the pulse instead of a vertical line is not the only advantage to be gained from using a timebase; if the repetition rate is made smaller then just a part of the wave will be spread across the whole screen. This allows any part of the wave to be examined in more detail.

COMPLETING THE OSCILLOSCOPE — THE TUBE CONTROLS

In order to make the electrons travel along the cathode ray tube a voltage must be applied between the cathode and the anode. If the cathode is made negative and the anode kept at zero voltage then the electrons, when they leave the oxide surface of the cathode, are attracted by the anode and shoot down the tube. For this reason the arrangement of cathode and anode is usually called an *electron gun*. The anode is made in the form of a tube so that it does not stop the moving electrons. The electron beam is 'squeezed' just before it reaches the anode so that the electrons form a narrow beam which passes along the middle of the tube. The squeezing is brought about when its electrons pass from a 'focusing anode' to the anode proper. This focusing anode is a hollow cylinder whose voltage is kept negative compared with that of the final anode. The greater its difference in voltage between its focusing anode and the final anode the more will the electrons be forced into a narrow beam. Hence all that is needed to control the focus is a resistor with a sliding contact on it as shown on page 116, varying the voltage.

The brightness (or the *brilliance* or intensity) of the spot depends on the number of electrons in the beam. This can be controlled in just the same way as the focus. The number of electrons which get through depends upon the voltage of the 'grid'. In this case, however, in order to stop electrons getting through the grid, its voltage must be

A typical cathode-ray oscilloscope, connected to show the waveform of an A.C. signal of a few volts, at a frequency of about 2 Kc/s.

much more negative than for focusing. The only other essential tube controls are the X and Y shifts which apply a steady voltage to the X and Y plates giving the spot a steady deflection. Quite a small voltage on the deflection plates will move the spot across the screen so the voltage across the shifts need be only quite small. It can now be seen why the control components are arranged in the particular way they are. The brilliance control needs a high negative voltage so it is connected near to the negative high voltage terminal; the focusing control comes next since it also needs a large negative voltage (but not so large as that of the brilliance control) while the X and Y shifts which need only a small voltage are connected last.

For the second group of controls needed for the deflection plates, a direct connection is needed between a terminal on the front of the instrument and the particular plate. However, to move the spot, the voltage applied to a plate must be of a certain size and, quite often, the oscillating voltages which are fed into the instrument are not large enough. Hence, two *amplifiers* are included and

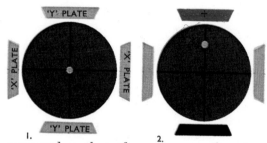

1. 2.

arranged so that, if necessary, pulses to each pair of plates can be amplified (increased in size) before they reach the plates.

Pentode valve amplifiers are used since they give a larger amplification than those using triode valves. For the X plates the pulses from a *timebase* are usually required, so provision must be made for connecting a timebase circuit to the X plates. Hence a 3-way switch from one of the X plates is arranged with possible connections to (1) the time-base, (2) the X terminal on the front of the instrument through the amplifier and (3) the X terminal direct. Also, a flyback quench and a synchronization control are included as part of the time-base circuit.

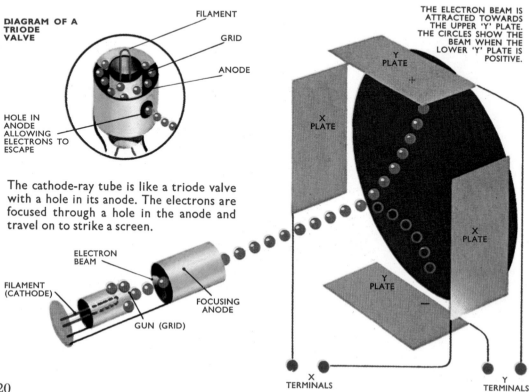

DIAGRAM OF A TRIODE VALVE

FILAMENT

GRID

ANODE

HOLE IN ANODE ALLOWING ELECTRONS TO ESCAPE

The cathode-ray tube is like a triode valve with a hole in its anode. The electrons are focused through a hole in the anode and travel on to strike a screen.

ELECTRON BEAM

FILAMENT (CATHODE)

GUN (GRID)

FOCUSING ANODE

THE ELECTRON BEAM IS ATTRACTED TOWARDS THE UPPER 'Y' PLATE. THE CIRCLES SHOW THE BEAM WHEN THE LOWER 'Y' PLATE IS POSITIVE.

Y PLATE

X PLATE

X PLATE

Y PLATE

X TERMINALS

Y TERMINALS

120

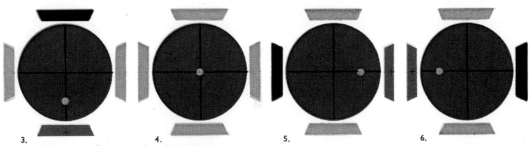

Diagram showing the fluorescent screen with D.C. voltages applied to the plates.
1. No signals on either plates, and the beam is not deflected. 2. A battery is connected across the 'Y' plates, making upper plate positive. 3. The battery is connected the opposite way round. 4. The battery is removed and the spot of light returns to the centre of the screen. 5 & 6. The battery is connected across the 'X' plates.

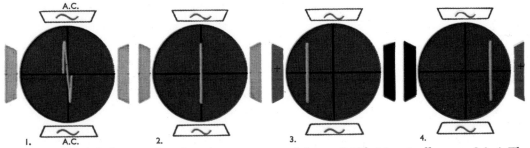

1. A.C. on the 'Y' plates makes the spot move up and down. 2. What is actually seen. 3 & 4. The line is moved by D.C. voltages on the 'X' plates.

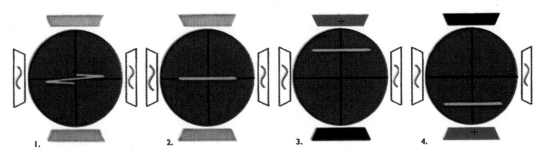

An A.C. signal on the 'X' plates moves the spot horizontally. D.C. on 'Y' plates moves line.

There are many modifications which can be made to this simple cathode ray oscilloscope to improve it and increase its versatility. Yet even this simplest form of oscilloscope has a property which no other scientific instrument can match —it can show the shape of a rapidly repeated, regular voltage pulse.

By using special circuits, pulses of only $\frac{1}{1,000,000,000}$ of a second duration may be displayed, and examination of the trace can tell us the duration and size of the pulse.

USING AN OSCILLOSCOPE

The labelling on the knobs of an oscilloscope is by no means standard, and can be confusing. But operating an oscilloscope is straightforward once its knobs have been identified with moving a spot of light up or down, left or right, making it appear brighter or in focus, or changing the frequency at which it darts across the oscilloscope screen.

The X and Y shifts which move the

121

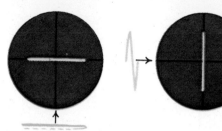

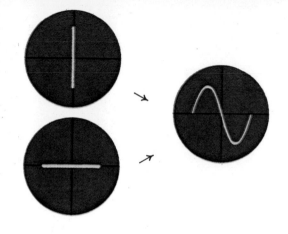

The sum of a saw-tooth wave on the 'X' plates and a sine wave on the 'Y' plates is a sine wave on the screen.

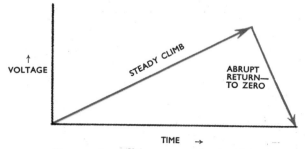

↑
VOLTAGE

STEADY CLIMB

ABRUPT RETURN— TO ZERO

TIME →

One cycle of the saw-tooth time-base wave which is applied to the 'X' plates.

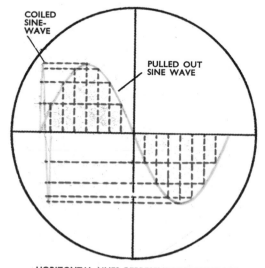

COILED SINE-WAVE

PULLED OUT SINE WAVE

HORIZONTAL LINES REPRESENT THE TIME-BASE WAVE AND VERTICAL LINES A SINE-WAVE ON THE 'Y' PLATES. THEIR RESULTANT IS A SINE-WAVE ON THE SCREEN.

spot over the screen are sliding resistance contacts. When the resistance is changed, the voltage on the plates changes, and the negatively charged electron beam is deflected. Brightness and focus knobs also operate variable resistors, but the voltages they control are much higher than the X and Y shifts.

A variable resistor is found behind the fine frequency control knob, but the coarse frequency control knob switches from one *capacitor* to another to alter the discharge rate, and hence the time base of the oscilloscope.

When the time-base and signal frequencies are not the same, the wave appears to move across the screen.

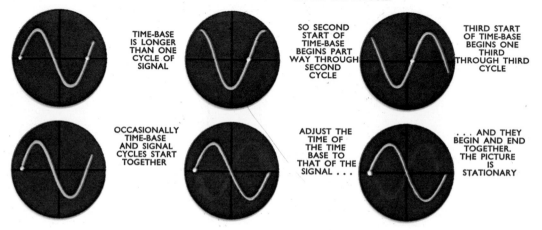

TIME-BASE IS LONGER THAN ONE CYCLE OF SIGNAL

SO SECOND START OF TIME-BASE BEGINS PART WAY THROUGH SECOND CYCLE

THIRD START OF TIME-BASE BEGINS ONE THIRD THROUGH THIRD CYCLE

OCCASIONALLY TIME-BASE AND SIGNAL CYCLES START TOGETHER

ADJUST THE TIME OF THE TIME BASE TO THAT OF THE SIGNAL . . .

. . . AND THEY BEGIN AND END TOGETHER. THE PICTURE IS STATIONARY

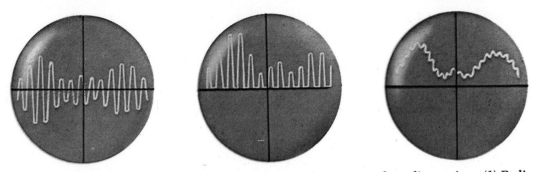

Typical oscilloscopic traces of electrical signals in various stages of a radio receiver. (1) Radio frequency amplitude modulated signal selected by the tuner; (2) the same signal after detection; (3) the final signal to be fed to the audio amplifier.

Using the oscilloscope to measure signal voltages has already been explained. The voltage at any part of the wave can be found from its height, and the sensitivity range in which the oscilloscope is working. Many oscilloscopes have screens marked in small squares to make measurement easier.

To measure the frequency of a signal, the leads for carrying the signal are connected, as usual, to the 'Y' and 'earth' terminals. If the signal originates in the electricity mains (its voltage suitably lowered by a resistor so that it does not damage the oscilloscope), then the wave trace will appear to move across the screen until the fine frequency control is turned to '5' and the coarse frequency control knob is switched to the 10 cycles per second range. In other words the frequency of the saw-tooth time base wave is now 50 cycles per second, the

same as the frequency of the alternating voltage from the mains (in Britain). One complete sine wave appears on the screen.

If, for example, the time base frequency is 49 cycles per second, then each cycle takes a fraction of a second longer than the signal cycle, and by the time the saw-tooth wave first reaches the right of the screen, the 50 cycles per second signal cycle has finished its first cycle and has already started on its second. The 50 cycles per second signal gets a little farther ahead of the 49 cycles per second signal every cycle. In fact, it moves ahead of the time base 49 times per second, and, because the eyes cannot follow individual traces, the result is that the wave appears to move across the screen.

When the fine frequency control is turned down to read 25 cycles per

If the repetition rate of the timebase is made half as fast as that needed to display one pulse, then two pulses can get to the Y plates between each flyback and so two pulses are seen on the screen (diagram A). If the repetition rate is made twice as fast then only half a pulse will get to the plates before the beam flies back. Then for the first half of the wave a 'hump' is traced out by the spot on the screen, while for the second half there is no pulse at the Y plates, so the spot will move horizontally across the screen. Then in the next half wave a hump appears followed by another line and so on. In practice the line and the hump will both appear so frequently that our eyes will only see the 'D turned on its side' shape (shown in diagram B) which is made up of both parts.

By varying the timebase any number of pulses can be shown on the screen. However, the pulse cannot be spread out by an unlimited amount since this would require that the repetition rate should be made very, very fast. In fact, in the timebases described the thyratron limits the repetition rate to less than 20,000 pulses per second.

A

B

123

second, the wave becomes stationary once more, and two complete waves appear on the screen. In fact, the waves stop moving when the X (time base) and Y (signal) frequencies are simple multiples of one another (e.g. at 6·25 cycles per second, 8 waves on the screen: at 12·5 cycles per second, 4 waves on the screen). The readings from the coarse and fine frequency controls, and the number of complete cycles on the screen together give the frequency of the signal applied to the Y plates. It is not difficult to see that *frequency=time base frequency* multiplied by *number of waves on the screen*.

COMPARING FREQUENCIES WITH AN OSCILLOSCOPE

It is sometimes required to compare the frequencies of two alternating currents, and this may be done very accurately using a cathode ray oscilloscope. To do this, one of the alternating currents is fed to one of the X plates, and the other to a Y plate of the oscilloscope. The trace which results will enable an observer to obtain an accurate value of the ratio of

If a *saw tooth* wave form is put on the X plates of an oscilloscope, and *no signal* is put on the Y plates, then a *straight line* trace results.

the two frequencies.

This might be used to find the frequency of oscillation of an electronic oscillator. If the oscillations of unknown frequency are fed to the X plates, and the signal from another oscillator of known frequency (the 'standard' oscillator), to the Y plates, then the pattern which results will provide the information required.

The trace on the oscilloscope will be

PICTURES FOR RATIOS
SLIGHTLY LESS THAN 1:1

Imagine that the screen looks like I at first. Then, after a short time it will look like II and, after another short time, like III and so on until it gets to the picture on the far right. This is just the same as I and the pattern is then repeated again.
This lagging of one pulse behind the other is effectively what happens when one of the frequencies is slightly less than the other. If the ratio of the two frequencies is slightly less than 1:1, then the picture on the screen

PICTURES FOR SIMPLE RATIOS
OF THE TWO FREQUENCIES

The frequency of the two pulses coming into the oscilloscope need not be the same. Different pictures appear for different frequency ratios. The simplest shapes of a few of these are shown here (where, for example,

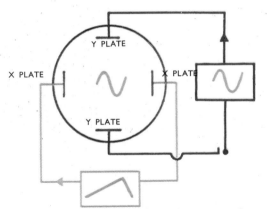

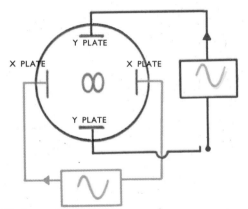

If a *saw tooth* wave form is put on the X plates, and an *alternating current* wave form on the Y plates, then the trace of the *alternating current* wave form results.

If *alternating current* wave forms are put on both the X and Y plates, then a *Lissajou Figure* results.

changing continuously, but by adjustment of the standard oscillator a stable trace results, which provides the value of the unknown frequency.

The kind of pattern obtained is called a *Lissajou Figure,* after Jules Lissajou, a French physicist (1822-1880) who first observed patterns of this sort in vibrating bodies. The sort of Lissajou figure obtained depends on the sizes and frequencies of the oscillations compared.

When the frequencies of the two oscillations are the same (i.e. the ratio is 1:1), a simple pattern is obtained, but when higher ratios 2:1, 3:1, etc., are involved the patterns on the oscilloscope become more complicated. However, every ratio has a pattern of its own, and if the frequency of the standard is known, then the unknown frequency may be found.

Often, if the standard oscillator can

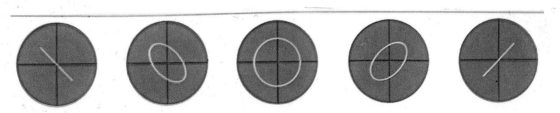

will change continuously from a straight line to an ellipse and then to a circle. After this, as the two pulses gradually come together again, the circle changes back into an ellipse and finally a straight line. Both of these slope in the opposite direction on the screen. Straight away after this the pattern starts to change back again, through the ellipse and the circle to the line sloping in the original direction, and then starts going back again.

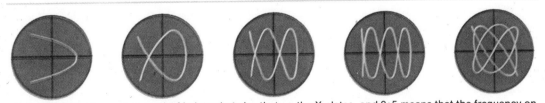

2:1 means that frequency on the Y plates is *twice* that on the X plates, and 2:5 means that the frequency on the Y plates is ⅖ times that on the X plates). These *Lissajou Figures* tell us what the ratios of the two frequencies are, because for each ratio there is a characteristic trace or pattern on the oscilloscope.

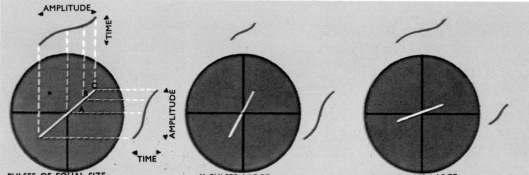

PULSES OF EQUAL SIZE | Y PULSES LARGE | X PULSES LARGE

How do the pulses arriving at the X and Y plates affect the spot on the face of the cathode ray tube? To understand this, consider two pulses of equal frequency arriving at the two plates at the same time. Then, as the size of both pulses increase, the spot will be drawn both upwards and outwards to B and then to C.

After both the pulses have reached maximum size and the pulses are getting smaller again, the spot can move back along the line to the centre of the tube and then out to the other side as the pulses increase into the opposite direction, before returning to the centre once more.

Alternating currents in electronic apparatus often have frequencies of thousands or even millions of pulses each second and the spot will move back and forth across the screen for each of these pulses. Our eyes are not able to follow the spot when it moves so quickly and a line will be seen on the screen.

produce pulses of the same frequency as the other unknown pulses then the frequency of the standard is varied until the easily recognised 1:1 pictures appear on the screen. Then the frequency read from the dial of the standard oscillator is exactly the same as the frequency of the other, newly built, one. Hence, by connecting the two oscillators to the oscilloscope and making only adjustment, the unknown frequency can be read off the dial of the standard oscillator. The shapes on the screen change quite quickly if the two frequencies are not the same as the standard, so that the oscilloscope provides a method of finding frequencies which is both easy to carry out and very accurate.

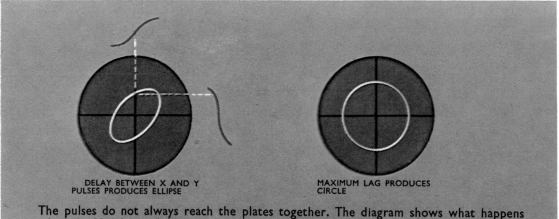

DELAY BETWEEN X AND Y PULSES PRODUCES ELLIPSE | MAXIMUM LAG PRODUCES CIRCLE

The pulses do not always reach the plates together. The diagram shows what happens when the X pulse is almost up to its maximum and the Y pulse is just starting. The spot no longer passes through the centre of the screen but moves round, tracing out a rugby ball shape (called an *ellipse*). If the arrival of one set of pulses is made to lag more and more behind the arrival of the others, then the ellipse on the screen widens out until it forms a circle (when the pulses are exactly opposite to each other).

END BAND OR BODY (FIRST FIGURE)	SECOND BAND OR TIP (SECOND FIGURE)	THIRD BAND OR FIRST SPOT (NUMBER OF NOUGHTS)	FOURTH BAND OR SECOND SPOT (TOLERANCE)	FIFTH BAND (STABILITY)
0	0	NONE 10 – 100 OHMS	1%	HIGH-STABILITY RESISTOR
1	1	1 100 – 1,000 OHMS	2%	Resistors used in electronic circuits can usually be identified by bands or spots of colour painted on them. Each colour stands for a number. For instance, black always stands for 0, brown for 1 and red for 2. The colour codes for the first two bands are the same. The third (which denotes the number of noughts after the first two figures) is slightly different. Gold or silver bands show that the resistor is less than 10 ohms. A gold or silver fourth band denotes a 5% or 10% tolerance resistor.
2	2	2 1,000 – 10,000 OHMS	3%	
3	3	3 10,000 – 100,000 OHMS	4%	
4	4	4 100,000 – 1,000,000 OHMS	GOLD – 5%	
5	5	5 1,000,000 – 10,000,000 OHMS	SILVER – 10%	
6	6	6 10,000,000 – 100,000,000 OHMS	NO FOURTH BAND OR SECOND SPOT – 20%	
7	7	7 100,000,000 – 1,000,000,000 OHMS		
8	8	GOLD – MULTIPLY BY 0·1 1 – 10 OHMS		
9	9	SILVER – MULTIPLY BY 0·01 0·1 – 1 OHMS		

Variations of the body-tip-spot and end-to-centre band systems.

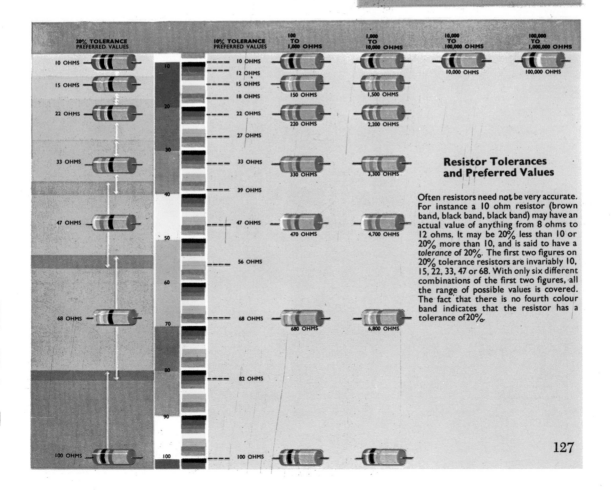

Resistor Tolerances and Preferred Values

Often resistors need not be very accurate. For instance a 10 ohm resistor (brown band, black band, black band) may have an actual value of anything from 8 ohms to 12 ohms. It may be 20% less than 10 or 20% more than 10, and is said to have a *tolerance* of 20%. The first two figures on 20% tolerance resistors are invariably 10, 15, 22, 33, 47 or 68. With only six different combinations of the first two figures, all the range of possible values is covered. The fact that there is no fourth colour band indicates that the resistor has a tolerance of 20%.

20% TOLERANCE PREFERRED VALUES: 10 OHMS, 15 OHMS, 22 OHMS, 33 OHMS, 47 OHMS, 68 OHMS, 100 OHMS

10% TOLERANCE PREFERRED VALUES: 10 OHMS, 12 OHMS, 15 OHMS, 18 OHMS, 22 OHMS, 27 OHMS, 33 OHMS, 39 OHMS, 47 OHMS, 56 OHMS, 68 OHMS, 82 OHMS, 100 OHMS

100 TO 1,000 OHMS: 150 OHMS, 220 OHMS, 330 OHMS, 470 OHMS, 680 OHMS

1,000 TO 10,000 OHMS: 1,500 OHMS, 2,200 OHMS, 3,300 OHMS, 4,700 OHMS, 6,800 OHMS

10,000 TO 100,000 OHMS: 10,000 OHMS

100,000 TO 1,000,000 OHMS: 100,000 OHMS

INDEX